PELICAN BOOKS

EDITED BY V. K. KRISHNA MENON

Advisory Editors: H. L. BEALES, Reader in Economic History, University of London; W. E. WILLIAMS, Secretary, the British Institute of Adult Education; SIR PETER CHALMERS-MITCHELL, C.B.E., F.R.S., F.Z.S., DR.SC., LL.D., Secretary of the Zoological Society 1903–1935

ESSAYS IN POPULAR SCIENCE
BY JULIAN HUXLEY

PELICAN BOOKS

ESSAYS
IN POPULAR SCIENCE

BY

JULIAN HUXLEY

Professor of Zoology
In the University of London (King's College)

PUBLISHED BY
PENGUIN BOOKS LIMITED
LONDON

First published SEPTEMBER 1926
First issued in the Phoenix Library 1929
Reprinted 1933
Published in Pelican Books MAY 1937
Reprinted AUGUST 1937

TO THE MEMORY OF

GEOFFREY SMITH

MY OXFORD TUTOR, KILLED IN THE EUROPEAN WAR
—A YOUNG MAN, BUT ALREADY A GREAT BIOLOGIST

MADE AND PRINTED IN GREAT BRITAIN FOR PENGUIN BOOKS LIMITED
BY PURNELL AND SONS, LTD. PAULTON (SOMERSET) AND LONDON

PREFACE

SOME men of science seem to think it desirable to offer an apology for a volume of popular essays on their own subject. I do not share this view. One of the duties of scientific men—not necessarily of all of them, but certainly of some of them taken as a group—is to make available to the lay public the facts and theories of their science, and especially to try to re-create something of the mental background that is engendered by those facts and those theories.

There is a danger, in these days of manifolded information and broadcast amusement, that the world will become divided into those who have to think for their living and those who never think at all. I am not speaking of those necessary but limited processes of thought needed to accomplish some routine of business, but the real thinking which does not stop until it has enquired *why* and *how* of the most familiar facts and processes, and insisted on exploring the foundations of belief. The true philosopher or man of science (as well as the true man of letters or the true statesman) is thinking new thoughts, or at least seeking the material for new thoughts, every day of his life. Meanwhile the occupation by which the average man is gaining his livelihood is becoming more standardised in its conditions, more limited in its scope, more definite in its routine. In the morning he reads his syndicated news and imbibes his millionfold-disseminated opinions. In the evening he goes to the cinema, or turns on his wireless set, or (if rather old-fashioned) manipulates his gramophone; in any case he again receives impressions which are being or have been scattered broadcast to millions of other human beings, and, what is more serious, he is presented with his impressions, whether by newspaper, cinema, radio, or whatever else, in a form demanding the minimum of thought, and indeed usually (like smoking) an agreeable substitute for that painful process of cerebration which solitude or personal contacts might otherwise engender.

Science herself is over-specialised: her right hand knoweth not what her left hand doeth; scientists in bulk inhabit a city of water-tight compartments. Each of them is busily engaged in investigating the interior of his own compartment; but by the irony of the situation, the compartments are not quite water-tight, and each investigator finds that the results of some one else's investigations sooner or later percolate into his own place, and often transform the whole aspect of his interior in such a way that much of his former descriptions turn out to be useless. . . .

Then there are insistent prophets who foretell the breakdown of scientific knowledge under its own weight; and there is no doubt that the burden of mere fact is enormous. As greatest difficulty of all, however, there remains the relation between scientific discovery and general thought. It takes so long for ideas to filter across in their true form; so often what comes through is the idea without its background—in other words, quite a different idea. But there is even more than that. Whenever the lag in communication between science and general thought grows considerable, whenever science, through laziness, pride, or pedantry, fails to make herself understood, and whenever the public, through laziness, stupidity, or prejudice, fails to understand, then we shall proceed to a lamentable divorce. It will not be merely the results of science which will not be assimilated, but science herself and the spirit of science will not be understood; and scientists will become an isolated caste in a half-hostile environment.

All these pictures I have drawn have been of the gloomy side. It would be perfectly possible to draw equally true pictures in a cheerful vein, pointing to the increase in the rate of scientific discovery, the general thirst for information, the growth of scientific endowment; yet there is undoubtedly a gloomy side, or at least a gloomy possibility, to the situation. The possible isolation of science, through its very increase of bulk, through its penetration to regions beyond the ken of common-sense, and through the temper of mind required of its votaries, is a real danger. Further, the more democratic the general civilisation, or, to be more accurate, the more rapid the process of democratisation in our present type of society, the greater is the danger.

But if any excuse *were* needed for the publication of these essays and articles, I should happily possess it. After giving lectures or addresses on scientific subjects I have always been asked by some among my audience when I was going to print them. Without such grateful encouragement from my auditors I do not suppose, in spite of genuine belief in the need for the popularisation of science, that I should have been stimulated to take the extra (and, may I add, often considerable) trouble needed to convert notes for a spoken address into written form, or to revise occasional articles so as to make them a little more worthy of a book.

The two longest of the following articles have not appeared before. 'The Frog and Biology' was a lecture delivered to the Nature Study Union at University College, London, in January 1925. The final long chapter on 'The Tadpole: a study in developmental physiology,' is based on a lecture given to Section D of the British Association at its Liverpool Meeting. 'Elixir Vitae' and 'Why do more Boy Babies Die than Girls?' are also here published for the first time.

Of the others 'Heredity: I' appeared in *The World's Work*; 'Heredity: II' in *Discovery*, as did 'Birds and the Territorial System,' and 'The Determination of Sex'; 'Biology in Utopia' in *Nature*; 'The Meaning of Death' in the *Cornhill*; 'The Inheritance of Acquired Characters' in the New York *Saturday Review*; 'The Control of the Life-Cycle' in *The English Review*; 'The Dominant Sex' and 'Birth Control' in *The Spectator*; 'T. H. Huxley and Religion' in *The Modern Churchman*; 'An Hour's Psychology' in *The Nation and Athenæum*; 'On the History of Science' in *The Observer*; and 'Evolution and Purpose' in *The Beacon*. To the editors and proprietors of these journals I offer my thanks for their kind permission to reprint.

In addition, I should like to thank the editors, authors, and publishers for permission to reproduce a number of figures from the following journals and books:—*School Science Review* (Figs. 6 and 7), John Murray; *The Journal of Heredity* (Figs. 5 and 9A), The American Genetic Association (and the *Journal of Experimental Zoology*, and Dr. Max G. Schlapp); Prof. C. M. Child's *Individuality in Organisms* (Fig. 14), and *Physiological Foundations o Behaviour* (Figs. 15 and 17), the University of Chicago Press;

Dr. L. T. Borradaile's *Manual of Elementary Zoology* (Fig. 8), the Oxford University Press; Professor D'Arcy Thompson's *Growth and Form* (Fig. 20), the Cambridge University Press (and Sir Donald Mac-Alister); and Prof. R. C. Punnett's *Mendelism* (Figs. 2 and 3), Macmillan & Co. Ltd. (and *Discovery*).

There is at the present day a growing interest in biological science. This is seen not only among the lay public, not only in the applied sciences of medicine, of plant and animal breeding, of agriculture and economic entomology, but also in the revolt against the one-sided arrangement by which physics and chemistry alone represent science in the average school curriculum. Physics and chemistry are sciences; but in the minds of the majority of schoolboys and school-girls there must be rooted the unfortunate idea that ' Science ' *is* Physics and Chemistry.

The chief concern of man up to the present has been with his environment. He has had to tame nature and harness her forces. To do this effectively he has had to learn to think scientifically about those forces: the result is epitomised in physico-chemical science and its brilliant application.

To-day and in the future, man's chief concern must be increasingly with himself. With his very success in the conquest of the environment has come a new danger. Unless the civilised societies of to-day improve their organisation, unless they invent and enforce adequate measures for regulating human reproduction, for con-trolling the quantity of population, and at least preventing the deterioration of quality of racial stock, they are doomed to decay and to be submerged in some new barbarian flood. To achieve this man must at last consent to think scientifically about himself and the intimate facts of his life, instead of surrounding every vital problem with taboo or prejudice; and in this task, biology must be his chief servant.

It is therefore of some real importance that the public interest in biology shall not flag: and if this little book in any way helps to maintain that interest, it will have served its purpose.

I would like to express my particular thanks to Miss G. S. Somerville for drawing a number of figures specially for this volume.

LONDON, *August* 1926.

CONTENTS

FIGURES IN TEXT

ESSAYS IN POPULAR SCIENCE

HEREDITY

I. THE BEHAVIOUR OF THE CHROMOSOMES

THE Greeks had a special word to denote remorseless destiny:
Até. The word is often translated fate; but we use *fate*
with a milder meaning, as if (which is indeed the case) we
only half believed in it. Much of Greek tragedy is imbued
with this idea of a power, felt but not apprehended, feared
but not understood, which shadowed and obstructed the
striving and the desires of humanity.

During last century, pioneer workers in the field of
heredity often came to regard its power as something very
like that of the Greek Até; as something which accumulated
the sins of the forefathers within itself, to charge their grievous
burden upon the children's shoulders.

This gloomy point of view naturally carried the seeds of
its opposite within itself. A prominent disciple of M. Coué
recently said to me, 'I don't believe in heredity'; and though
this ostrich-like burial of one's head in the sand of disbelief
is carrying matters to extremes, there are many to whom
the idea of a hereditary force pushing men blindly along
predestined roads is hateful, who react to their dislike by
belittling and discounting its power and extent.

But science takes no account of likes or dislikes; its
business is to find out the truth, to discover what things
are, and how they work. Before we can profitably discuss
what part heredity should play in our philosophy of life,
we must first descend into the workshop of living reality
and see what machinery is there at work. To speculate
without facts is to attempt to enter a house of which one has
not the key, by wandering aimlessly round and round,
searching the walls and now and then peeping through the
windows. Facts are the key. Biology, during the last half

11

century, and especially during the last twenty years, has provided us with a mass of facts—results of long-continued breeding tests, of patient observation through the microscope, of ingenious experiments—which are unlocking many secrets of heredity.

It would be useless in the short space I have at my disposal to try to present the evidence which biology has amassed. All I can attempt to do is to try to give a picture of the results achieved. Imagine then that you have found yourself in a world which, by some unknown power, had been magnified to such a vast extent that an ordinary blood corpuscle was of the size of an elephant. Or, what comes to the same thing, imagine yourself minified to a degree which would enable you to creep into the cells of the body as if they were rooms in a house. It is perhaps as well to remember that to do this your height would have to be about one-millionth of what it originally was and your weight accordingly reduced a million billion times. What then would you see? When you had penetrated the membrane which surrounds every cell you would find yourself in a chamber chiefly filled with that semi-fluid mixture of substances which we call protoplasm. Suspended within it would be a great sphere or ovoid bounded again by a resistant wall or membrane. Within this would be a substance called chromatin, arranged in a dense network, and bathed by a more liquid stuff.

This you would see in almost any cell of the body; but in addition each sort of cell would probably contain other special structures or substances. A muscle cell, for instance, would show a great scaffolding of those fibres whose contraction makes muscular movement possible. The gland cell, in the sweetbread or in the salivary gland, would show you drops, large or small, of the chemical substance which it was manufacturing for the good of the body. A cell of the liver, in a well-fed animal, would be crowded with lumps of glycogen, the substance into which sugar is transformed for purposes of storage

But if growth is to proceed or if the wastage of cells which die and wear out is to be replaced, new cells must continually be produced, and this, as a matter of fact, is always accomplished by the division of previously existing cells into two.

If you happened, in your new diminished existence, to come upon a cell at such a time, you would be presented with a strange spectacle which would keep you standing before it as long as it continued and leave you puzzling over its significance (Fig. 1, *f-k*). As a first preliminary you would see the wall of the nucleus beginning to break down; meanwhile the network of chromatin within would condense, become more solid, contract, and finally separate into a number of thick strands, or we had better say ropes, of chromatin, lying about bent and haphazard at the place where the nucleus had been. You would see that along the length of each of these bodies there was arranged in orderly succession a great number of smaller units; probably several hundred in each strand, not arranged side by side, but one after another like beads on a string. Gradually you would see that each of these beads, or lesser units, would divide into two, and that by this means would each of the fibres would simultaneously be split along its whole length. Other strange changes, however, would have been taking place while you were watching. A small, rather dense body that you might have noticed originally outside the nucleus in the resting cell would have been seen to split in two, and round each of the halves of it a curious radiating appearance would have become visible. This radiating appearance is due to some effect exerted by each half of the granule upon the living substance of the cell, turning it from a more liquid into an almost solid state. This influence radiates out, naturally enough, in all directions, and so a star-like figure of these almost solid strands comes into being round each half of the granule. Meanwhile, the two halves move apart from each other. The fibres between them, like iron filings between the poles of a magnet, become bent so that a spindle-like appearance is presented, and finally the whole figure, with its spindle in the centre and its two star-like masses of radiating fibres at its two ends, comes to extend across the whole of the cell.

As it did so, you would have seen the ropes of chromatin gradually arrange themselves, in obedience to some unknown force, round the centre of the spindle. Some of the fibres of the spindle would get attached to the chromatin strands, which by this time would have been divided along

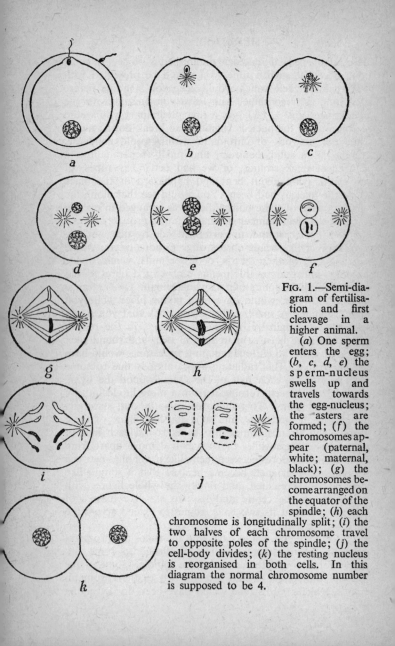

Fig. 1.—Semi-diagram of fertilisation and first cleavage in a higher animal.

(a) One sperm enters the egg; (b, c, d, e) the sperm-nucleus swells up and travels towards the egg-nucleus; the asters are formed; (f) the chromosomes appear (paternal, white; maternal, black); (g) the chromosomes become arranged on the equator of the spindle; (h) each chromosome is longitudinally split; (i) the two halves of each chromosome travel to opposite poles of the spindle; (j) the cell-body divides; (k) the resting nucleus is reorganised in both cells. In this diagram the normal chromosome number is supposed to be 4.

their length. And now the fibres which had been made fast
would begin to contract, the two halves of each chromatin
rope would be pulled slowly apart from each other, and
slowly the two sets of halves would be separated to the two
poles of the spindle. Just so could one imagine ropes being
made fast to bales in a ship's hold, and, at a word of
command, a crane coming into action and pulling the bale
out to where it was wanted; only here, there is no word
of command, no directing beings, but all proceeds in
silence and by virtue of the inherent properties of living
matter.

As the half-strands proceed to the two sides of the cell,
you would see them begin to lose their sharp outline, to
swell, to become less solid, and finally to branch and inter-
lock with one another to form a network; and meanwhile
the radiating fibres would become shorter and vaguer, and
eventually, with some change in the central granule, disappear altogether. The network arising from the chromatin
strands would become more and more irregular, would
swell, would form a tough membrane round itself, and
would thus at last come to resemble an ordinary nucleus
again. Meanwhile you would have been surprised to see
a furrow appearing all round the cell, deepening gradually,
and finally cutting the single cell into two halves in such
a way that each of them would possess one nucleus and one
granule. So the process would be complete, and two cells
be made out of one: growth alone is now needed for each
to become identical with its parent.

If you were to travel round the body (whether of man,
or animal, or plant) into which you had penetrated, and
were to see many cells dividing, you would find that the
number of chromatin strands present was always the same;
while if you explored a number of different organisms, you
would find that each had thus its constant and characteristic
number. You would also usually find that that number
was an even one, and that the chromatin strands fell into
a series of similar pairs.

But your discoveries would not necessarily end here: you
might be lucky enough to be a witness of the process of
reproduction, and you would see that what is usually called
the ' beginning of a new life ' is really not that at all, but

the handing on of life, the original and only article, to a new individual (Fig. 1, *a-j*).

You would see, if the organism you were exploring were a mammal, a female reproductive cell or egg which, in spite of its being minute in comparison with the egg of a bird or even of a frog, would to your million-fold diminution be as big as a vast skyscraper. Then you would see enormous numbers of a strange new sort of cell, each with a main piece or ' head' not much larger than yourself, armed forward with a piercer, and propelled from behind by the violent lashing of a formidable length of tail. Million upon million of these sperm (as they are called), a huge rushing horde, would be seen swimming past you; as they approached the egg-cell, you would see them converge upon it, swim round and round it, and finally one of them would succeed in burrowing right into its substance. On this, the egg-cell would cease to attract the others, and they would swim aimlessly about until their death—the failure of millions for the success of one. Meanwhile you would see the ' head' of the successful sperm begin to swell up within the egg, transform itself into an ordinary-looking nucleus, and approach the nucleus of the egg. The two nuclei, now together, would be seen to break down into chromatin strands, radiations and a spindle of fibres would grow out, each chromatin strand would split lengthwise, and half of each would go to either side, as before, in the ordinary tissues of the body.

If you had thought of counting, however, you would have found that the egg-nucleus and sperm-nucleus each produced only half the ordinary number of strands, and that each contained only one member of each pair of strands. In other words, the nucleus of an ordinary body-cell contains two complete sets of chromatin strands; and one set has come from the mother *via* the egg, and the other from the father *via* the sperm.

Egg and sperm, therefore, must have undergone some process by which the ordinary number of strands is halved, the two sets separated from each other. If you were to attempt to discover more on this point, by penetrating back along their history, you would as a matter of fact discover that at one of the divisions very shortly before the final production of eggs and sperms, instead of the chromatin strands splitting lengthwise, there had been first a union of the members of a pair of strands, then a separation of one whole strand from the other member of the pair (Fig. 2, p. 44).

In these glimpses of the appearance and disappearance of the chromatin strands, their accurate halving at ordinary cell-divisions, their sorting out into two similar sets before reproduction, the union of two sets again at fertilisation, you would have been viewing the actual distributive machinery of heredity.

This machinery can actually be seen through the microscope. The chromatin and the chromatin strands, or chromosomes as they are generally called, have the property of staining very deeply with various dyes, and so being readily visible; and every stage of the process has been minutely described for many different animals and plants.

In your imaginary diminished state, you would have seen much more than any microscopist has yet seen; he is limited to magnifications of one or two thousand diameters; and to work with these, even with the best of microscopes, is no easy task. Nevertheless, the general facts are perfectly clear and well-established.

HEREDITY (*continued*)

2. CHROMOSOMES, MENDELISM, AND MUTATION

THE latest advance in general biology has been the discovery that inheritance takes place by means of separable units, generally known as unit-factors or *genes*. It is effecting the same sort of revolution in our biological thinking that Dalton's realisation of atoms as the units composing chemical substances did for chemical thinking a hundred years ago.

The facts which have been elicited by microscopical observation have been briefly sketched in our first article. Practically all of them have been discovered in the last fifty years. Much of the earlier work, especially on the meaning of the observations, was done by Germans, prominent among whom were Flemming, Weismann the great evolutionist, Boveri, and the botanist Strasburger. In later years England has produced well-known workers in this field in the persons of Doncaster and Farmer, and America in E. B. Wilson, Sutton, M'Clung and others.

When these facts concerning chromosomes were first discovered, the theory was promptly advanced that it was by means of the chromosomes that inheritance was to be explained. The ovum and sperm differ from each other in almost every particular of size and shape and constitution. There is only one point in which they agree, and in that they are identical: both possess one complete set of chromosomes. It was therefore natural to suppose that it is by means of these chromosomes that organisms—whether plants, animals, or human beings—inherit characters equally easily, as we know they do, from their mother's or their father's side. We shall see later that this theory has been abundantly justified by the facts that have since been discovered.

Meanwhile, let us not think too much of theories, but merely of the established fact that all higher living things possess in every cell of their body two complete sets of chromosomes, one coming from the father, one from the mother, and that each of these is accurately divided every time that a cell divides.

While one set of workers was establishing these facts, others were engaged on extensive plant- and animal-breeding experiments, with far-reaching results.

Enormous numbers of crosses between different varieties of both animals and plants were carried out during the nineteenth century, and a number of general conclusions arrived at. But there remained a feeling that we had only scratched the skin of the problem, without any real penetration of its hidden secrets. Then, in 1900, a dramatic event in scientific history took place. Two independent workers, reading through the literature on the subject in the hope of hitting on something to illuminate their results, happened upon an account of some experiments carried out and recorded as far back as 1866 by the Austrian, Gregor Mendel, Abbot of Brünn (Brno). These had lain unproductive for half a century, like seed in a box. Now at last they were to germinate. Both men realised their importance; they have served as the basis of all the enormous advance that has since been made; and there has sprung into being a new science, of animal- and plant-breeding carried out on the Abbot's principles, and called Mendelism in his honour.

What were the new principles that proved so illuminating? Put as briefly as possible, they are as follows. Wherever one variety of an animal differs from another variety in a constant and well-marked way, these differences can be shown, by cross-breeding experiments, to depend on a definite number of separate characters which can be passed on from parent to offspring—in other words inherited—and each of which can, by proper crosses, be separated from the others. An example will make this clear. There are two races of fowls, the one black, the other white with black splashes. When crossed together, all their offspring in the first, or, as it is often called, the F1[1] generation, are alike; but they do not resemble either parent. This form of fowl is bluish-black with black lacing, and is called the Blue Andalusian. If these Andalusians are bred together, the next, or F2, generation will consist of three different sorts of fowls—white exactly like their white grandparents, black exactly like their black grandparents, and Andalusian exactly

---

[1] F1 stands for *1st filial*, F2 for *2nd filial*, and so on: P1 stands for *1st parental*, P2 for *2nd parental* or *grand-parental*, etc.

like their parents. These will always appear, if a sufficient number is bred, in the same proportion, the whites averaging 25 per cent., the Andalusians 50 per cent., and the blacks 25 per cent. Mendel, as a matter of fact, worked not with fowls, but with different strains of peas, but got essentially similar results. The explanation he gave was that something which made the black fowls black was present in their reproductive cells, and so handed to their offspring; while in white fowls, a slightly different but corresponding something was handed on in the same way. These ' somethings ' may be called *factors*, and the appearances they produce in the adult fowl *characters*. When whites are crossed with blacks, the fertilised egg receives one white-producing and one black-producing factor. The resulting character is neither black nor white, but a compromise, the bluish colour of the Andalusian. When the Andalusian fowls come to reproduce, the Mendelian theory supposes that all the reproductive cells will receive either a black-producing or a white-producing factor, *but not both.*

Let us for convenience call the former B and the latter *b*. There are, then, four possibilities for the next generation. A sperm with B can equally well fertilise an ovum with B or one with *b*; and the same two possibilities are open to sperms containing *b*, and each of these unions is equally likely to occur. Thus on the average, out of every large lot of resulting fowls, one-quarter will contain B+B, one-half B+*b*, and the last quarter *b*+*b*. But B+B will give a black fowl, B+*b* an Andalusian, and *b*+*b* a white. We thus have an explanation both for the sorts of fowls produced in the F2 generation, and of the proportions in which the different sorts occur. In subsequent generations the F2 whites will breed true like the original pure white strain, the blacks breed true like the original black, and the Andalusians will give the same results as their F1 Andalusian parents (see diagram, p. 22).

Another character in which breeds of fowls may differ is the shape and size of the comb. If two breeds, one with the ordinary high comb (so-called single comb), the other with a rose comb (a low comb with little warts on it), are crossed, we shall get results essentially similar to those found in the Andalusian fowl. The second, or F2, generation will consist of 25 per cent. of birds which will breed true to single-comb shape, 25 per cent. which will breed true to rose-comb shape, and 50 per cent. which will contain one factor for each of the two comb-shapes, and therefore will not breed true.[1]

The question immediately arises, What will happen if a white bird with a single comb is crossed with a black bird with a rose comb ? Will the white colour and single comb shape stick together, or shall we be able to separate and recombine them ? The answer given by experiment is that recombination is possible. In the F2 generation, we shall get two new pure-breeding types—white birds with rose combs, and black birds with single combs—as well as types like the original parents, and types that do not breed true (see diagram, p. 23).

Similar results have been obtained by the hundreds of thousands of crosses which have been made during the last twenty years with Mendel's principle in mind, and we can assert, without any fear of contradiction, that for the majority of characters which go to make up any species or race of animal or plant, and to mark it off from other species, the fundamental laws laid down by Mendel hold good.

Curious results are obtained when a hereditary factor acts as the foundation on which other factors can build. For the ordinary colour of a wild mouse to appear, for instance, *at least* three factors are necessary—one for colour, called C; one for producing black pigment, B; and one for producing a yellow band on the hairs and so giving a grey effect, G. If, instead of G, only the recessive *g* is present, there will be no yellow bands, and the mouse will be black; if further only the recessive *b* is present instead of B, the mouse will be chocolate-brown. But if the recessive *c* is substituted for C, no colour at all will be produced, and the mouse will be white, whatever combinations of B or *b*, G or *g* it may possess.

We can represent the mouse's hereditary constitution as regards colour by a formula. CC.BB.GG is a grey, CC.BB.*gg* a black, CC.*bb*.*gg* a chocolate, CC.*bb*.GG a chocolate-grey, and all animals possessing *cc* are albino.

[1] In this case the F1 all have combs of the rose type. Here we say that the rose type and factor are *dominant*, the single *recessive*. These F1 rose-combed birds are indistinguishable in appearance from birds pure for rose-comb, but do not breed true, being of constitution R*r* instead of RR.

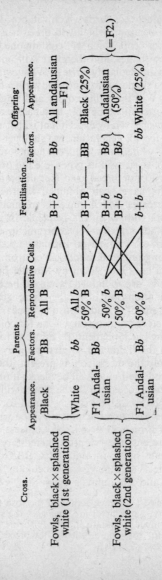

| Cross. | Parents. | | | | Fertilisation. | | Offspring |
	Appearance.	Factors.	Reproductive Cells.			Factors.	Appearance.
Fowls, black × splashed white (1st generation)	{ Black	BB	All B		B + b ——	Bb	All andalusian = F1
	{ White	bb					
Fowls, black × splashed white (2nd generation)	F1 Andal-usian	Bb	{ All b / 50% B		B + B ——	BB	Black (25%)
	F1 Andal-usian	Bb	{ 50% b / 50% B		B + b —— / B + b ——	Bb / Bb }	Andalusian (50%)
			{ 50% b		b + b ——	bb	White (25%)

(= F2.)

Cross	Parents			Fertilisation	Offspring	
	Appearance.	Factors.	Reproductive Cells.		Factors.	Appearance.
Fowls, black and rose comb × splashed white and single comb (1st generation)	Black, rose	BB . RR	All B . R	B . R + b . r ——	Bb . Rr Andalusian, rose (= F1).[1]	
	White, single	bb . rr	All b . r			
F1 × F1	F1 Andalusian, rose	Bb . Rr	25% B . R 25% B . r 25% b . R 25% b . r			
	F1 Andalusian, rose	Bb . Rr	25% B . R 25% B . r 25% b . R 25% b . r			

From these gametes, besides combinations which will not breed true, we shall, in F2, get BR + BR = pure for black and rose, like one grandparent; b . r + b . r = pure for white and single, like the other grandparent; but also B . r + B . r = pure for black and single; and b . R + b . R = pure for white and rose—*i.e.* two new pure-breeding strains.

[1] These fowls have a rose comb, as rose is *dominant* to single; *i.e.* rose appears even when only one R is present. R*r* birds, therefore, *appear* rose-combed, but do not breed true for comb-shape.

This has a curious consequence. A mouse with the formula $cc.bb.GG$, although white, is carrying the factor for grey, ready to act as soon as opportunity offers. If this mouse is crossed with a black one, the offspring will contain one C factor, one B factor, and one G factor, and, since all these are dominant, will all be grey like ordinary mice. It is like the appearance of the image on the photographic plate when the developer is added. This atavism, or reversion to an ancestral type, is not uncommon when different varieties are crossed, and receives its explanation through Mendelism.

To be brief, we may say, first, that all the characters of a species are controlled in their development by definite units or factors, which can be handed on from parent to offspring. Secondly, that all such factors are present in pairs, one being derived from the father, the other from the mother. Thirdly, that when the reproductive cells are formed, the two members of a pair separate from each other, so that each sperm or each ovum must contain one member of a pair, but cannot contain both; and, finally, that different unit-factors are inherited independently of each other, so that, by making the right series of crosses, we can build up new races or varieties of animals by combining factors for characters of different existing breeds. All kinds of characters have been shown to be inherited by means of unit-factors—colour, shape, size, fertility, vigour, resistance to disease, abnormality, length of life. The external environment may often modify the way in which a character develops; but the basis which can be modified at all, and the limits of the extent to which it can be modified, are provided by the factors and their influence during development.

Through Mendel, the idea of the unit-factor was introduced into the study of inheritance. By the labours of innumerable workers, some of the best-known of whom are Bateson and Punnett in England, Baur in Germany, De Vries in Holland, and Morgan in America, his principles have been shown to hold good for every sort and kind of characters, in every sort and kind of organism, including man himself.

We shall next see how the most recent work is combining the facts drawn from a study of the chromosomes with those connected with inheritance by unit-factors.

So far we have been dealing with facts and principles

which, though once the subject of heated dispute, are now accepted as proven by all biologists. In the present one, we are touching on discoveries so recent as to be still in the region of controversy. The principles here set forth, however, though still not accepted by many men of science, are rapidly gaining ground, and are being used as a basis by the majority of research workers in heredity. The writer believes them to be true in all essentials, and certainly to be far better as a working hypothesis to guide our future advance than any others now in the field.

In our study of unit-factors, we saw that one of Mendel's laws asserted that unit-factors were inherited independently of each other. This was the original form of the law, and is true for many factors. But as animals were bred on a large scale, and single species were worked on in an intensive way, so as to study the relation of a great many separate factors to each other, exceptions were found which have made it necessary to restate the law. In its new form, it runs as follows: (1) Unit-factors are inherited in groups. Factors in separate groups are inherited independently, but those in the same group are *linked* in their inheritance.

(2) These groups of factors are not inherited entirely *en bloc*, but, though the factors within each group are linked together, the linkage is not absolute. In other words, the factors of one group tend to be linked together in inheritance; but the linkage is not complete, and is of varying intensity for different factors. (3) The number of groups is constant for any particular species.

Into the details of the second of the three points we will not now enter. It is the fact that a constant number of independent groups of factors do exist (and this is undoubted) which interests us for the moment.

It will be remembered that observation with the microscope revealed the fact that a constant number of chromosomes was also present in each species. It is, therefore, a natural question to ask whether there is any relation between the number of group and the number of chromosomes. So far, on account of the enormous amount of time and labour involved in carrying out the requisite number of breeding experiments, the question has only been actually answered for one genus, though researches with the same end in view are in progress on many animals and plants. The one form where a definite answer has been obtained is a tiny fly called *Drosophila*, the fruit-fly.[1] This is particularly suitable for breeding experiments, as it can be easily kept; it has large broods of offspring, and a new generation appears about once a fortnight. In *D. melanogaster*, Morgan has now records of several million flies, all with known pedigree. To obtain a record of the same number of generations in man, we should have to go back before the dawn of history. Something like four hundred variations, or *mutations*, have cropped up spontaneously in his stock, and the inheritance of most of these has been worked out. The result has been to show that there are four groups of factors, which is the same number as the number of pairs of chromosomes. Further, the number of factors so far found in each group is roughly proportional to the length of the different chromosomes as seen under the microscope. Morgan and many others, therefore, conclude that the physical basis for the unit-factors is to be found in the chromosomes. If one single factor were to be found not linked to any of the four existing groups, the whole theory would have to be given up, as it would be impossible to reconcile five factor-groups with four pairs of chromosomes. On the other hand, a related species, *Drosophila virilis*, possesses six pairs of chromosomes, and six linkage groups of factors have been found in it, and in *Drosophila obscura* the five discovered linkage groups tally with the visible five chromosome pairs.

Other facts connected with linkage indicate strongly that the unit-factors are arranged in a row along the chromosomes, like beads on a necklace. In this, therefore, we have an explanation of the facts observed in the division of chromosomes.

From Morgan's work in New York on *Drosophila*, it seems almost certain that when the two chromosomes of a pair unite before the formation of gametes, they sometimes twist round each other and break across. If so, the pieces then join up again, but after an exchange of partners, so that each of the resulting chromosomes is made up of one piece derived from one of the original members of the pair, the rest derived from the other. If the factors are arranged along the chromosomes, then the nearer two factors

[1] It has also been recently made almost certain for the Sweet Pea.

lie in a single chromosome, the less chance there is of their being separated from each other when this process of *crossing-over*, as it is called, takes place, so that the closeness with which factors stick together in inheritance—the strength of linkage, as we say technically—should be a measure of their actual distance apart on the chromosome.

Working on this hypothesis, Morgan has been able to construct a map of the chromosomes of the fruit-fly, on which are plotted the positions of the four-hundred-odd hereditary factors yet investigated in the animal. Of course the map, instead of being reduced like most maps with which we have to deal, is enormously enlarged. Microscopic objects are measured in microns, each of which is the thousandth part of a millimetre; and even though the longest chromosome in the fruit-fly is only about 3 or 4 microns long, yet we can be sure that it contains at least several hundreds, and probably several thousands, of these separate, living, self-reproducing factors or genes.

What is more, each factor always keeps its place in one particular chromosome, and at a particular spot within that chromosome. The chromosomes of one of the higher animals thus reveal themselves as the most complicated piece of chemical machinery known to science. They are composed of thousands of separate particles, each of them capable of exerting a particular effect on the developing animal, but all bound together in a definite arrangement and in unvarying proportions—a living necklace, each bead different from every other, all tied together in a definite order and pattern, and thus the guardians of the general hereditary constancy of the race.

Of the exact way in which these factors exert their effect during development we are still almost wholly ignorant. Biology is in about the same position that chemistry occupied when Dalton's inner vision showed us the atom and the molecule as the units of chemical combination. A glimpse has been revealed of the kind of machinery that is at work. This, in chemistry and physics, led rapidly to an enormous extension of our control over lifeless matter; new processes were discovered, new compounds built up from the elements to serve human purposes. It is inevitable that the same increase of control will follow in the realm of living things; only here, because of the greater complexity of the problems and the greater labour involved in keeping and breeding animals for experiment, it will take longer to achieve an equal result.

From another point of view the study of heredity is bound up with that of variation. All living things vary—that is, the different individuals of a species differ from each other; and it is clear that only through the fact of variation is Evolution possible. Thus it is of the greatest importance to know what are the causes of variation, and whether all variations are heritable. Great strides have been taken in this field too during the last twenty years. We can now theoretically, and in many cases actually, distinguish definitely between 'mutations,' which are due to changes in the constitution of the animal—in the hereditary factors themselves —and 'modifications,' which are due to changes in the environment, and cause the same constitution to develop in a different way from the normal.

If one were to take a random lot of several thousand beans of the same garden variety and weight them, one would find that the weights could be arranged in a continuous series, beans with weights near the average being the most numerous. If one were to breed only from the heaviest beans, in the next generation the average weight would be higher; and if this process were repeated for several generations, the average would go up very considerably. Eventually, however, it would stop increasing and further selection would have no effect.

This was carried out in practice by the Danish botanist Johannsen, who, by his further analysis, enabled us to understand the reason for the facts. Beans are self-fertilising; so that if, instead of treating the sample as a whole, he kept the beans produced from each plant separate, he could be sure of dealing with a hereditarily pure stock, or as it is usually called, a pure line. He then found that each pure line showed a certain range of variation in the weight of the bean it produced, but that selection within a single pure line had no effect: whether he bred from the lightest or from the heaviest beans of one pure line, the *average* weight of the descendants was always the same.

The interpretation of these results is this: the hereditary constitution of each pure line, the sum total of its factors, is a constant quantity. The observed differences in weight

shown by the beans produced by a single pure line are due
to external factors—the degree of nourishment in the soil,
the amount of rain, the position of the bean in the pod,
of the pod on the plant. These 'modifications' do not alter
the hereditary constitution of the stock any more than
freezing or boiling alter the chemical composition of water,
although they so profoundly alter its appearance and properties for the time. In the first experiment, where an alteration
of average weight was produced by selection, all that was done
was to isolate certain pure lines with high average weight from
a large assortment of lines with very various average weights.

Numerous other experiments of a similar nature have
been made and similar conclusions reached. The main
result, enormously important not only for animal and plant
breeding, but also in its applications to human heredity,
is that so-called ' acquired characters,' in other words
modifications caused by the environment, and those resulting
from use and disuse of organs, are either not inherited at
all, or else to such a slight degree as not to be of any great
importance in heredity and evolution. Docking dogs' tails
for generations does not cause the birth of puppies with
shorter tails, any more than the muscular development
resulting from blacksmith's work produces better muscular
development in his children. Chinese women are not born
with abnormally small feet; nor would an English child
brought up in France by French foster-parents have any
more tendency to speak English than would a French child.

What then is the cause of the variability which, as Darwin
and his successors showed, is universal in nature ? What is
the cause of the differences between the pure lines which
Johannsen used ? What is the origin of all the differences
in character which are inherited according to the laws of
Mendel in wild and domestic animals and plants ?

If a pure stock, whether of animal or of plant, is inbred,
we get a pure line, or at least a line which is pure for many
characters. Every now and then, however, one or a few
individuals of the stock will be found to be different from
the rest. When tested by breeding, the peculiarity is almost
always found to be inherited according to Mendelian rules.
In other words, what has happened has been that a single
hereditary factor has altered, and altered permanently.

Such an alteration in the hereditary constitution is now called a mutation. Mutations have been seen to occur in many animals and plants. The most extensive series have been observed in our friend *Drosophila*. This little insect has red eyes and a grey body. Mutations giving white eyes, pink eyes, miniature eyes, no eyes at all—yellow and black body-colour —curved wings, short wings, rudimentary wings—different arrangements of bristles and hairs—an extra pair of legs— different degrees of fertility—different length of life—different resistance to unfavourable conditions and to disease— different instincts—all these and many others affecting every sort of character, whether physical or mental, structural or physiological, have been seen to originate in pedigreed cultures to breed true, and to be inherited according to Mendel's laws.

As a result of these and many other observations, we are now in a position to assert definitely, first, that whenever a difference between two varieties or species is found to depend on a Mendelian hereditary factor, we can be reasonably sure that the difference of character was originally brought about by a mutation in a single factor. In general, the mutation will be in one of a chain of factors; then the result produced by the whole chain is affected, *e.g.* a mutation in the colour-producing factor C of the mouse can give albino mice, but the difference between albino and grey mice depends on at least three factors, not on one only. Secondly, this apparently spontaneous change or mutation of single factors has been and still is probably the most important source of the new departures without which evolution could not take place.

The most obvious mutations are those which produce large effects; and it has naturally been these which up to the present have been chiefly studied. But there is good reason to believe that very small mutations, producing small quantitative changes in size, in shape, in growth, in fertility, in activity, have made the most important contribution to evolution.

That difference in size may be due to a number of Mendelian factors, whose differences in their turn must be due to mutations, is shown by various breeding experiments. When, for instance, two races of tobacco plant with very different size of flowers are crossed, the first generation has flowers which are uniform in size and intermediate between the

flowers of the parents. But when a second generation is
raised from these plants it presents a very great diversity
of flower-size, the small and large sizes of the original parents
being recovered or even surpassed. From this assemblage,
varieties could be obtained which bred true and showed
different degrees of flower-size. This means that the difference
in size between the flowers of the parent stocks was due to
several Mendelian factors, each one of which causes a slight
amount of increase in size. On no other supposition can
one explain the uniform and intermediate first generation
followed by the great range of diversity in the second, and
the segregation of true-breeding stocks in it. Similar results
have been obtained with different-sized strains of such
diverse organisms as fowls and maize.

If it is the hereditary constitution which determines what
any animal or plant shall be, then even the differences between
species should be due to differences in Mendelian factors.
Where the offspring of species-crosses are perfectly fertile,
this often seems to be true. When two wild species of snap-
dragon, for instance, were crossed, the first generation
was very uniform and showed characters intermediate between
those of the two parents. But in the second generation an
overwhelming variety of types appeared, differing from the
two original species in colour, shape, size, habit of growth, and
every other conceivable character. True-breeding stocks could
be obtained from them, and there was no escaping from the
view that the differences between the original species were due
to differences in a considerable number of factors; a difference
in fifteen factors would give over thirty thousand types in the
second generation, and this is approximately what was found.

We must now ask what bearing these discoveries have
upon human heredity. It is of course impossible to conduct
controlled breeding experiments on man, and without these
it is often impossible to determine the inheritance of a
character. But we know that certain well-marked characters
(such as eye-colour, or the abnormal condition known as
brachydactyly, in which the joints of the fingers are one too
few) are inherited in Mendelian fashion, and we know that
man possesses chromosomes; and we can have every con-
fidence that the laws found to hold good throughout higher
animals and plants will apply also to him.

If such is the mechanism of heredity, such the process of variation, it remains to ask what conclusions we are to draw as to the way in which evolution has occurred.

It was supposed by Lamarck, the great French zoologist of the beginning of the nineteenth century, and by his followers, that acquired characters were regularly transmitted and that their inheritance was the chief factor in evolution. It is known that use strengthens and disuse weakens many organs; that the stomach of a sea-gull fed on corn will become hardened and thickened to cope with the unaccustomed food; that many animals and plants have quite a different appearance according as they are brought up in the warm or in the cold, in damp or dry surroundings; that training and effort are necessary to intellectual and moral achievement. It seemed therefore natural to think that changes produced in this way should be handed on to future generations; and by many it was felt that if they were not thus handed on, then half the spur to human effort would disappear.

But facts take no account of what we human beings think or desire; and with the establishment of the pure line idea, and the discovery that the hereditary constitution consisted of definite units of living substance arranged in a definite way along the chromosomes, the matter took on a different aspect. In the first place, it was definitely shown that many acquired characters were *not* inherited. And secondly, it became clear that the real problem before us was to discover how to alter the hereditary constitution at will.

In the past, Evolution seems to have depended mainly on the random occurrence of all sorts of mutations, and the selection and survival of such organisms as possessed mutations which were favourable in the struggle for existence. Man must aim at replacing this slow-working machinery by one more rapid, this blind and accidental process by one inspired with conscious purpose.

But *revenons à nos moutons*—to our chromosomes. We may sum up by saying that the hereditary constitution of any organism consists of a great number—probably thousands in the higher animals—of unit-factors arranged in two single rows or series inside the nucleus; that this series is cut up into what we see and call the chromosomes, for the sake of convenience of handling at cell-division, etc.; and that the presence of one series—in other words, of one set of unit-factors—is necessary for development to occur and for characters to be handed on from parent to offspring.

It will be seen that the observed fact of the chromosomes being present in pairs fits with the fact of unit-factors being present in pairs, and that the reduction of the chromosomes explains how only one of each pair of unit-factors is present in any of the reproductive cells.

If the reader has had the patience to follow the discussion till now, he will see that a new way of looking at animals and plants is opened to our intellect. We must think of them, in the first place, as being produced by the interaction of a great number of separate particles of living substance, the factors, each one a separate unit in the original fertilised egg, and each one capable of undergoing lasting alteration (mutating) quite independently of the rest. Secondly, we must think of ourselves and other organisms as being essentially double, with a complete set of these units from father and mother alike. Thirdly, since these units can be inherited more or less independently of each other, sexual reproduction means first a reshuffling of the factors, and then a recombination of them in new arrangements. In other words, if a useful variation in one character has occurred in one animal, and one in another character has occurred in another, sexual reproduction gives the opportunity for these two separate useful characters to be combined in a single breed. (In passing, it may be remarked that this is probably a reason for the almost universal occurrence of sexual reproduction both in animals and plants.) Fourthly, we know that these mutations in single factors are constantly happening. At present we do not know how to produce mutations; but the belief that we shall eventually be able to do so underlies our work, and once we have discovered the way, our knowledge of the laws of heredity will enable us to build up improved races of animals and plants as easily as the chemist now builds up every sort and kind of substance in his laboratory. In a word, Mendelism made it possible for us to represent the hereditary composition of an organism by a *formula*. Morgan's recent work is making it possible to represent that composition by a *structural formula*.

B

THE INHERITANCE OF ACQUIRED CHARACTERS[1]

THE inheritance of acquired characters is not only a question of the greatest theoretical interest, but also one of outstanding practical importance, since with it many educational and social principles and practices stand or fall. It is worth while to summarise how, to most biologists, the problem of acquired characteristics and their inheritance looks to-day, since the discoveries and analyses of the last quarter-century really put the matter in a new light. It is no longer of any use to discuss it from the standpoint of Lamarck or even of Weismann—any more than it would profit to discuss the transmutation of the elements from the standpoint of the alchemist or even of Mendeléef or any other worker of the pre-radium era.

Thanks to the discoveries of Mendel and their later extension by workers such as Bateson and especially Morgan, we can now identify with certainty what Weismann could only guess at, and Darwin not know of at all—the physical basis of inheritance. This is constituted by the so-called chromosomes (word as yet unfamiliar to the man in the street, but which he will have to learn like *atom* or *electron*), or by some part of them. The chromosomes are elongated bodies, and along their length is stretched the stuff of heredity. This is composed of units, the so-called Mendelian factors, which are arranged in a definite order down the line, so that each factor is not only lodged in a particular chromosome, but has its particular and unvarying station within that chromosome. Alternations in factors (' mutations ') produce characteristic effects on the characters of the animal, different kinds of effects for different factors. Thus so far as we can see, the hereditary constitution consists of definite chemical units, united in constant proportion and position, and combining to make the development of the animal

[1] From a review of *The Inheritance of Acquired Characters*, by Dr. Paul Kammerer, translated by A. P. Maerker-Branden, New York, 1924.

(or plant) proceed in just one particular way—when in a standard environment.

In a standard environment : this is where the next stage of the analysis begins. Some people who study education are so impressed with the environment's power that they ascribe everything to environment: while many who have had to do with the science or the practice of breeding make equally sweeping statements about heredity and its omnipotence. Both are quite wrong. In a sense *both* environment and heredity are omnipotent, for the best be-chromosomed ovum will only develop within certain limits of temperature, light and other environmental agencies; and other eggs in the best surroundings may die or give rise to monstrosities because of defects in their hereditary make-up.

What most people forget is that in this whole problem of the analysis of inheritance, we can only study *differences*. We see that two animals or plants are different from each other, and we try to discover the cause of the difference. Sometimes we find it due to a difference in the environment in which they grew up; sometimes to a difference in the hereditary factors with which they are provided: *voilà tout*.

It is clear that one and the same set of hereditary factors might react quite differently to different environments: for instance, fish which grow up normal when in normal sea-water possess but a single Cyclops eye when grown in magnesium chloride solutions; female ant-eggs on one kind of food become queens, on another soldiers, on another workers. Such facts are remarkable enough and important enough: but they are in principle no more remarkable than the fact that a pure paraffin wax remains solid below a certain temperature, but becomes liquid above it, or that sulphuric acid reacts with one metallic salt to give one result, with another to give another.

The extraordinary power of the environment over individual development is well shown by facts like the following. If a tendon like the Achilles tendon of an animal is cut, it will heal again. If, however, the calf muscle which pulls on that tendon is at the same time put out of action by cutting its nerve, the tendon does not heal properly, but only an irregular mass of connective tissue fills the gap. Finally, if in such an animal a silk thread is healed into the wound, and slight tension exerted on it day by day, a little tendon is formed along the thread—at right angles to the original tendon's course. It has long been well known that tendons are wonderfully adapted to their function, both as to their strength and their direction. We now see that we need not postulate special hereditary factors for each nuance, but that given the fundamental property of tendon-forming tissue to lay down its fibres along the lines of greatest tension, all the rest follows directly as the result of the strains which use and the form of the skeleton and the muscles put upon it. Similar principles hold good for the detailed architecture of bones, the size of muscles, the course of blood vessels and other 'functional adaptations' within the body.

All this, as you see, has nothing to do with inheritance. Fundamentally, the theory of the inheritance of acquired characters asserts that changes induced by the environment in the developing organism tend to become fixed in its hereditary constitution so that they eventually appear whether or not the same kind of environment that originally induced them is there or no.

It has also in recent years often been extended, in ways quite different from those imagined by Lamarck, its original promulgator, to ask simply whether the hereditary constitution can be affected from without. And this is really the best way to put the question, for it is the most general form in which it can be put, and the truly Lamarckian theories would constitute only special cases of it.

Can the hereditary constitution be permanently changed by environment? That, then, is our question. It is clear that, theoretically, it should be possible to induce such changes. The hereditary constitution is seen to be something material, which only our lack of knowledge prevents us from defining chemically; and as such it must be possible to alter it. The remarkable fact, however, is its stubborn resistance to alteration. Sixty-nine generations of flies bred in the dark, and yet no alteration in their eyes or their instincts with regard to light. Ninety generations of an attempt to raise their resistance to heat by acclimatisation and selection —without result; indefinite time spent by dandelions in the lowlands not preventing their reacting to mountain conditions immediately by changing size, form, and proportions—or *vice versa* on replanting from mountain to plain; the failure of tendons to form except under direct stimulus of tension (see above); the failure of children to learn their own language quicker than a foreign tongue—conditions of course being equal—*et cetera.*

When changes do occur in the germ-plasm, they are usually of the kind known as single-factor mutations. Great numbers of these have been described, especially by Morgan. Naturally they must have a cause; but so far, no one has succeeded in discovering what it may be, or relating the changes in any way to environment. So far as their connection with external conditions goes, these inner changes can only be described as spontaneous or random. Indeed, although each cell of the body normally contains two similar specimens of such Mendelian factor, mutation can be shown usually to occur only in one cell of the thousands in the body, and only in one of the two factors within that microscopic cell.

There are a few cases on record where treatment appears to have induced mutation and so caused hereditary change. Many of the experiments, however, were carried out without proper controls or full understanding of the pitfalls that lurk for the unwary in the interpretation of results, and, leaving for the moment Kammerer's own work on one side, we are left with perhaps a dozen or two dozen cases where the desired result *may* possibly have been achieved, but where reinvestigation is necessary for certainty; and three or four where it probably *has* been achieved.

What is emerging more and more clearly, however, is that even in the more probable cases the effect is rare and uncertain, affecting only a very few of the specimens submitted to the treatment.[1]

Now Dr. Kammerer claims himself to have experimentally demonstrated the inheritance of acquired characters in salamanders, in toads, and in ascidians. In the brief space at my disposal, and at the risk of seeming curt, I can only say that his work has not carried conviction to biologists as a whole, and in particular to those who ought to be best qualified to judge—the students of heredity, with Bateson, Baur, Morgan, Goldschmidt, and Johannsen at their head.

[1] *E.g.* Jollos's experiments with paramecium, Guyer's with rabbits, and Harrison's with moths.

No one has ever been able to repeat them, and distinguished workers like Herbst have obtained quite opposite results.

It is a sad thing when a man has spent half a lifetime on researches which his colleagues will not accept. However, let us not forget that it is not always the organised body of the science which is in the right ! Luckily in his experiments with sea-squirts he has given us something which can readily be repeated and tested ; and this is, I believe, now being done. Till then we must bring in a verdict of ' not proven.'

How difficult it is to be certain in such experiments is shown by facts such as these. A few years ago it was claimed that ' waltzing ' habits induced by rotating rats at high speed over long periods (an experiment primarily carried out with reference to the equilibration of aviators !) were inherited. Later painstaking repetition by one of the leading American geneticists has shown that the inheritance is probably apparent only, the motion causing a decreased resistance in the ear with consequent bacterial infection, which, once it had got a hold, infected subsequent generations, with the same result of running in circles. Or again, a year or so ago, the famous Russian physiologist, Pavlov, claimed that he had found the effects of training mice to be inherited, the animals needing fewer and fewer ' lessons ' to achieve a certain trick as the generations went on. Two independent American workers, however, have repeated the experiment with quite negative results. One possible explanation is that Pavlov, who had not previously worked with mice, mistook the effects of gradually improved treatment on tameness and health for true inheritance.

One is always asked what exists as a possible alternative to the inheritance of acquired characters if we wish to account for progressive change in evolution. It is strange that Darwin's theory of Natural Selection seems never to have been properly assimilated by the average man in its sixty-five years' life, especially now that the neo-Mendelians such as Morgan are finding such strong corroboration for its postulates.

If variation (mutation) occurs, as it appears to, in all directions, the struggle for existence will ensure that only those which are in the ' right ' direction shall be preserved.

The very real difficulty exists that the greater number of mutations whose occurrence has been observed have a deleterious effect. Even if we possessed a complete sample of the mutations that occur in a given time, this would be expected, since change is apt to throw delicate mechanisms out of gear: but we almost certainly have not a complete sample, since the mutations which exert striking and often monstrous effects are the most likely to be observed, while those which are likely to play a part in evolution, namely mutations of small extent, often affecting physiological character instead of structure, are very difficult to detect. It is, however, consoling to find that Mr. R. A. Fisher, the statistician, has demonstrated that very few favourable mutations are quite sufficient to provide the raw material for progressive evolution.

The great question is, of course, the genesis of the hereditary variations. As we have already seen, numerous mutations occur which assuredly have no definite relation to use or to environment. These must provide some of the raw material for selection. It is further highly probable that we shall find special cases in which the environment can be made to alter the germ-plasm, and that some of these alterations will be adaptive. But in spite of all the work that has been done, we have only established the very definite certainty that to a great many apparently potent outer influences the germ-plasm is quite unresponsive. The old Lamarckism is dead: the inheritance of acquired characters is of a certainty not the universal provider which it was once thought to be. It remains to be seen what the more restricted 'new Lamarckism' may finally bring forth.

THE DETERMINATION OF SEX

SEX appears to be absent in one great group of organisms, the bacteria. There are also here and there a few species of plants which only reproduce asexually—some kinds of banana, for instance, never set seed; it is therefore clear that sex is not a necessary accompaniment of life. Why, then, is it so widespread?

A partial answer at least is given by the well-known facts of Mendelian heredity. Through sexual reproduction, the factors in the chromosomes are at each generation shuffled and recombined in new arrangements; and this provides the possibility of combining separate advantageous mutations in a single stock. If, for instance, a tall pea with green seed-coat is crossed with a dwarf pea with yellow seed-coat, all combinations will occur in the second generation —tall yellow, tall green, dwarf yellow and dwarf green. If tallness and yellow colour happened to be more advantageous than dwarf size and green colour, then it is obvious that any race which possessed both these characters would be well placed in the struggle for existence. If crossing were impossible, such a race could only arise if both the favourable mutations were to occur in one line. To put it in the most general terms, we may say that, if x separate mutations arise in a species in a given time, then if sexual reproduction does not exist, the result will be $x+1$ varieties; but if it does exist, then by recombination 2^x varieties are possible. If the number of mutations had been ten, the number of varieties would be eleven in the one event, 1,024 in the other. The existence of sex thus obviously favours constructive change, and makes it possible for a species, if the conditions in which it finds itself alter, to adapt itself much more rapidly to them.

It has been supposed that sexual fusion of cells was accompanied by some mysterious rejuvenation, without which the race would die out. This, however, is becoming more and more doubtful. For one thing, it has been found possible by special treatment to keep various unicellular animals like the slipper animalcule (paramecium) reproducing by fission for apparently indefinite periods without any sexual process of conjugation occurring, although conjugation is a normal process in their life-history.

The evil effects of inbreeding were supposed to proceed from a similar lack of fresh blood, from the absence of that fusion of gametes from different stocks which normally happens in sexual reproduction. Here again we are now able to give a different and more satisfactory explanation. In an ordinary animal or plant, mutations are occurring all the time. Many of these are unfavourable—they represent little accidents to the factors, to the machinery out of and by which a normal organism is built up. But most of such harmful factors are recessive; that is to say, if they are carried by an individual which is also carrying the dominant factor of the same pair, no visible effects are produced; this is so, for instance, in the case of tall and dwarf peas, which when crossed give hybrids containing the factors for both tallness and dwarfness, and yet are indistinguishable by inspection from their tall parent. In a large cross-bred population, it will be only rarely that individuals containing two of these harmful recessive factors will be segregated out. But if inbreeding is practised, a little calculation will show that it will produce a number of different stocks, each of them pure for some particular combination of the various factors which were present in the original population. As a result, the recessive factors will segregate out pure, in double dose, in a number of these stocks, and will exert there any harmful effect they may have; and the general average of the population, in vigour, health, size, and fertility, will go down very considerably. But the poor types can now be rejected by the breeders; and the good types which are left are known to be pure and to possess no more harmful recessive factors. Thus, if the good types are now crossed together, a stock will be produced which is as good in appearance as the original, and has the further merit of not containing harmful recessive factors and therefore not continually producing a certain proportion of low-grade individuals. Thus the *immediate* effect of inbreeding on a large mixed population is bad; but if it is judiciously practised, it may be the best means of building up a pure healthy stock. That it cannot be always and inevitably bad is shown by the fact that there exist some animals and a number of plants in which self-fertilisation—the most rigid form of inbreeding possible—is the invariable rule. In brief, it may be said that our understanding of Mendelism has made it clear that in-breeding is only bad when hidden harmful factors exist in the stock, and that it is harmless and even good when the stock's hereditary constitution is a good one. The ecclesiastical prohibition of the marriage of near relatives is thus seen to be only conditionally justified on biological grounds.[1]

Two quite distinct processes are involved in the fertilisation of egg by sperm which occurs in the ordinary sexual repro-duction of man and most animals. First there is the fusion of two separate nuclei, two single sets of chromosomes, and the consequent shuffling and recombination of the hereditary factors. In the second place, there is what is usually called *activation*—the starting-off of the egg upon its career of growth and development. In most species, if fertilisation does not take place, the egg remains inert, and sooner or later perishes. However, in some animals, such as aphids (plant-lice) and water-fleas, the egg is capable of developing without this stimulus. Such forms are called parthenogenetic. The bee is of especial interest, since the males, or drones, are fatherless, produced parthenogenetically, while the queens and workers all arise from fertilised eggs. In the course of evolution, a change must have come about so that activation is no longer carried out by the sperm, but by some other means. What in these animals has happened naturally, has for others been accomplished artificially. In many creatures, such as sea-urchins and starfish, marine worms, molluscs, and even frogs, it has been found possible to make the egg develop without sperm. In sea-urchins the best method is immersion in certain chemicals; in starfish it is heat or shaking; in frogs it is pricking with an extremely fine glass needle which has been dipped in blood. The result is the same—that fatherless individuals are produced by man's intervention. Some of the fatherless frogs have

[1] The stimulating effect which often follows a cross between markedly different stocks, while also explicable in terms of factors, is due to rather complex causes. The reader is referred to the book by East and Jones, *Inbreeding and Outbreeding*.

been raised in the ordinary way, and are apparently healthy in every respect. This shows us that the sperm normally performs two functions: it contributes a quota of hereditary factors from the father to the developing embryo; and it activates the egg, probably by chemical means, to start its career of growth and division. This *artificial parthenogenesis* has so far only been tried upon animals which lay their eggs into the water before fertilisation; there can be no doubt, however, that it is theoretically possible in other forms, and that it would be only a matter of surmounting technical difficulties (although these would doubtless be very grave) to apply it to mammals and to human beings.

Whatever the original reason for the wide occurrence of sex, whether the greater plasticity it confers, or some more primal reason still, in any case, once it was established it reacted markedly upon the later history of life. The gametes are primitively alike; then a division of labour occurs, and the male gamete or sperm takes on the function of finding the female gamete or ovum, which is concerned with storing up food-material for the future development of the embryo; then the individuals which produce the different gametes became different in other ways, the male generally more active, the female generally more passive and concerned with the nourishment and care of the young. As mind develops, new complications arise; in the first place, the female requires to be courted and stimulated, her emotions roused, before she will yield to the male; from this cause there have arisen the elaborate and wonderful ceremonies and displays of courting animals, associated often with special colours and structures. Sometimes the result is grotesque, as in the wattles and bare coloured skin of the cock turkey, or the coloured posteriors of many male monkeys; more often the effects are striking, as in the gleaming metallic patches on the legs of many male spiders, displayed to best advantage during their strange courtship dances; or they are of real beauty, like the song of the nightingale or the thrush, the colours of the cock humming-bird, the plumes of the egret, the train of the peacock. It may be indeed said that the sense of beauty has mainly sprung out of the relation of the sexes, and that the actual beauty of animals, where it does not depend simply upon regularity of form, or upon the sense of power or of speed or of vitality produced on us by certain creatures, is due originally to the existence of individuals of separate sexes with emotions which must be touched before sexual union can be consummated. Finally, in man himself, recent work in psychology has shown that our instincts and the emotions associated

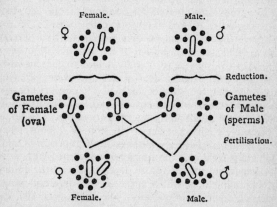

FIG. 2.—Diagram of reduction and fertilisation in an animal with XX-XO sex-determining machinery. The female has fourteen chromosomes, twelve ordinary chromosomes (autosomes) plus two sex-chromosomes (XX); the male thirteen, twelve autosomes plus one X. All the eggs will have 6+X, while of the sperms half will have 6+X, and be female-determining, half 6+O, and be male-determining.

with them are the driving force of our actions; that the most primitive instincts, such as those of fear and of sex, are perennially active in us; but that the human mind possesses the power called by psychologists the sublimation of instincts, whereby the instinct becomes directed towards other objects—its driving force harnessed to new, more exalted, and more spiritual ends. So fear becomes the basis of reverence and awe, the sexual instinct gives rise to the highest sympathy and most universal love.

Sex is thus intertwined, inevitably and fundamentally, with all our activities and with our very being. Man and woman differ from each other, not only in body but in mind; and such is our mental architecture that there are few activities of life in which the sex-instinct, however transformed and sublimated, does not play some part. It thus becomes of the greatest interest to discover the mechanism by which sex is determined, and to find out whether by any means we can bring it under our control.

To do this it is necessary to revert once more to the lower animals. In discussing heredity, we said that the chromosomes of any species were present in pairs, the members of each pair being similar. In a number of species there is an exception to this rule. In certain insects, for instance, while all the chromosomes of the female can be arranged in pairs, those of the male cannot. On closer examination, this is seen to be due to the fact that the male has one less chromosome than the female, and that therefore it only possesses one instead of two of one particular kind of chromosome. This sort of chromosome has been called the X-chromosome. When the female comes to form eggs, ordinary reduction occurs; the two members of each pair separate from each other, and all the eggs receive one X. In the male, however, the X has no mate to pair with; accordingly half the sperms will contain an X, half will be without one. If a sperm with an X fertilises an egg, the result will be XX—in other words, the constitution characteristic of a female; whereas if the ' no-X ' sperm fertilises an egg, the result will be X— in other words, a male. As the two sorts of sperm will be produced in equal numbers, an equal number of XX and X embryos will be formed, and this will result in an equal number of males and females (Fig. 2).

A similar state of affairs is to be found in many other animals, including cattle, horses, and pigs. In other cases, including man himself, the male, instead of possessing simply an unpaired X, has an unequal pair of chromosomes, one being like the two found in the female, and therefore called X; the other unlike, and called Y. Here again there will be two sorts of sperms; the X-bearing will produce females, the Y-bearing will produce males.

Let us now turn to the results of breeding experiments. Besides ordinary Mendelian inheritance, there has for some time been known another type, called sex-linked inheritance. An example will make this clear. A mutation producing white instead of red eyes was discovered in the fruit-fly Drosophila. When a white-eyed male is crossed with an ordinary female, all the offspring are red-eyed, showing that white is recessive. In the second generation, there appear 75 per cent. red-eyed animals and 25 per cent. white-eyed, as in a normal case of Mendelian inheritance—but the white-eyed individuals are all males. Still more strange, if the cross is made the other way, between a white-eyed female and a red-eyed male, a quite different result is obtained. In the first generation all the daughters are red-eyed like their father, and all the sons white-eyed like their mother; in the second generation, 50 per cent. are white-eyed, and males and females are equally affected.

The fruit-fly is one of those animals in which the male possesses one X and one Y chromosome. If we suppose that the Y is inactive—a supposition which is, as a matter of fact, borne out by other evidence—this curious and at first sight very puzzling form of inheritance is exactly what we should have to prophesy mathematically, if the factors for redness and whiteness of eye-colour were situated in the X-chromosome (Fig. 3). That this view is correct, at least for the fruit-fly, has been definitely shown. Certain stocks of the fly were found which gave exception to ordinary sex-linked inheritance. These exceptions were to be expected if, through some accident to the machinery of cell-division, animals were to have been produced which contained a Y in addition to two X's; and when the stock was examined microscopically, it was actually found that this was the case.

Exactly similar sex-linked inheritance is found in most other insects, in mammals, and in man himself. For instance, the human diseases known as hemophilia (habitual bleeding due to the inability of the blood to clot) and night-blindness are transmitted in this way. It is also found in some plants in which the sexes are borne on separate individuals. Since in Drosophila the association of sex-linked factors with X-chromosomes is certain, and in many other animals in which similar sex-linked factors occur, the male also possesses a single X, or an X and a Y chromosome, we may safely say that sex-linked inheritance implies the existence of sex-chromosomes different in the two sexes, and vice versa.

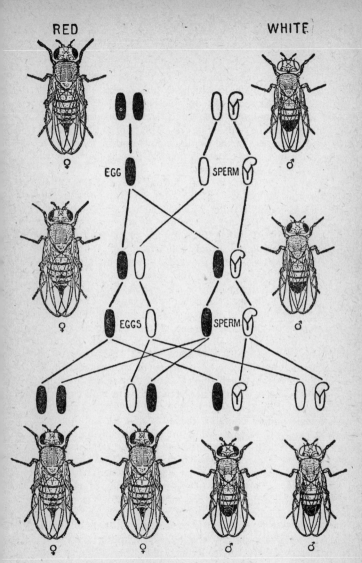

RED   WHITE

EGG   SPERM

EGGS   SPERM

FIG. 3.—Sex-linked Inheritance of White Eye in Drosophila. Females on left, males on right. The sex-chromosomes behaviour is represented diagrammatically; the X-chromosome bearing the factor for red eye is represented in black, that bearing the factor for white eye in outline.

(Reproduced from 'Mendelism,' by Professor R. G. Punnett, F.R.S., by permission of the Author and of Macmillan & Co., Ltd.)

It is a curious fact that in birds and in butterflies and moths, while sex-linked inheritance occurs, it is reversed; it is the female, not the male, in which sex-linked characters usually appear, and the facts can only be explained if we suppose that in these animals it is the male who possesses two X chromosomes, the female but one. This supposition has been proved to be true in the domestic fowl and in some moths, where the microscope reveals that the females have one less chromosome than the males.

From all the facts, we can, I think, be sure that all the higher animals possess special X or sex-chromosomes, two in one sex, one in the other, by whose agency sex is determined.

What must the precise action of this machinery be supposed to be? What, for instance, is its relation to the so-called secondary sexual characters, all those which, like the beard of man, the voice of the nightingale, the plumage of the pheasant, the sexual instincts of many animals, are different in the two sexes, but not directly concerned with the reproductive organs? Here again, recent research has given us a definite answer. The factors necessary for the development of the characters of both sexes are present in all individuals of any of the higher animals, but normally only those which are proper to one sex actually develop. The presence of one or of two X's acts like a switch, which alters the condition in the developing embryo in such a way that in one case only the male characters can reveal themselves, in the other case the female characters. A female animal contains, locked within the chromosomes of her cells, the factors which in other circumstances could combine to build a male, the male contains, never expressed in actuality, the constitution of a female. That this is so is shown definitely by the facts observed when two species are crossed. The males of different species of pheasants, for instance, differ from each other very much in plumage, while the females are all more or less drab and alike. If a female Reeves pheasant is crossed with a male of another race, the males among the hybrid offspring show many characters of the male Reeves pheasant, although these characters must have been transmitted through the chromosomes of the mother, in whom they were invisible.

In insects, the simple presence of one or two X's in the

cells of the body is enough to call forth the proper sex-characters; but in higher animals like birds and mammals, there is another link in the chain. This link is furnished by the reproductive organs. The sex-chromosome machinery acts as a switch which allows either male or female reproductive organs to develop in the embryo; but as soon as these are developed, they start producing a secretion or hormone which is necessary for the development of all other sexual characters. The most complete proof of this has been afforded by the extraordinary experiments of Steinach, Sand, Moore and others, who have removed the reproductive organs from young rats or guinea-pigs, and grafted into them reproductive organs taken from individuals of the opposite sex. The result has been a complete alteration in the animals' growth, ending in an almost complete assumption of the characters of the opposite sex. Male guinea-pigs whose reproductive organs have been removed and replaced by ovaries have even yielded milk and suckled young in the normal way, and show the sexual instincts proper to females. Such animals can, of course, not breed, since at the time of the operation the internal organs associated with reproduction were already laid down, and only the subsequent growth of the animals was affected.

Very interesting results have also been obtained on adult birds. Here it is found that the ovary secretes some substance which prevents the development of male plumage. A capon, or any male bird with reproductive organs removed, shows no alteration of plumage.[1] But a hen bird whose ovaries are taken out will at the next moult assume the plumage proper to the male. Further, there exist certain breeds of fowls, such as the Sebright bantam, in which the cocks are hen-feathered, and possess none of the special hackles and curved tail-feathers usually seen in cocks. This must be due to their possessing a secretion similar to that of an ordinary hen, for when their reproductive organs are removed, we find, paradoxical as it may seem, that they assume normal male plumage as the result ! In insects, as indicated already, removal of the reproductive organs has no effect upon other sex-characters.

[1] The comb and wattles, however (like the instincts), are under the control of the testis, and revert to a minute size in the capon.

We next come to certain strange abnormalities which throw considerable light upon our problem. Among insects curious individuals are found from time to time in which some part of the body—usually a half or a quarter—is male in character, while the rest is female. These are known as *gynandromorphs*. In ants, very remarkable appearances may result. The male ant is winged, the worker female wingless; and thus a gynandromorph may be winged on one side only (see Fig. 4).

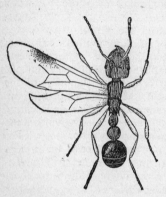

FIG. 4.—A gynandromorph ant; male on left, worker (sterile female) on right.
(*Re-drawn after Doncaster.*)

In the fruit-fly, not only the sex and the secondary sexual characters, but also the sex-linked characters may be different on the two sides. It has recently been shown that the gynandromorphs in the fly are really female in constitution, but that at one of the early divisions of the egg, one of the X-chromosomes lags behind and fails to get incorporated with the rest of the chromosomes. As a consequence, one of the resulting cells still has the proper complement of two X's, while the other has but one. The part with two X's becomes female; that with one, male. If the two X's were carrying different sex-linked factors, sex-linked characters also could be different in the two regions of the body. In mammals, these sex-mosaics, as we may call them, do not occur, because the substances secreted by the reproductive organs pass into the circulation, and influence the sexual characters equally all over the body.

An even more remarkable abnormality is provided by what are called intersexes. The gipsy moth, that terrible forest plague, has a well-marked variety in Japan. When this is crossed with the European race, very curious results are obtained. When a Japanese male is crossed with a European female, 50 per cent. of the offspring are normal males, but the remainder are intermediate between male and female—so-called *intersexes*. When these are carefully examined, it is seen (by an examination of their hard parts which, once formed, cannot be re-moulded) that they have started their development as females, but ended it as males. They are females which suddenly, during their growth, have by some invisible but inexorable power been switched over to become of the opposite sex. All degrees of intersexuality are known, according to the races employed in the cross. The females may show only the faintest traces of maleness; may be equally male and female; may be preponderatingly male; or finally, in certain crosses, the change of sex may come so early that no trace of female characters appears, and the cross results in males alone.

Even though half of these all-male broods ought by rights to be females, yet all behave like normal males, and can mate and produce offspring. With these experiments, carried out over a long series of years by Professor Goldschmidt, of Berlin, we can at last be sure that it is possible for a complete and functional reversal of sex to take place.

When the cross is made the other way, with a Japanese female and a European male, the first generation is altogether normal. But in the second generation abnormal individuals again appear. This time, however, they are different from those first seen, and on analysis turn out to be intersexual males—*i.e.* animals which have started as males and been forced to finish their development as females.

What is the explanation of these strange facts? It appears to lie, ultimately, in the different climates to which the different races are adapted. The Japanese races are adapted to grow more rapidly. The factor which produces maleness must lie in the sex (X) chromosome, which in moths is double in males, single in females. The factor producing femaleness we cannot yet locate so definitely; but it has been shown to be transmitted always and only through the mother; let us call it Q. Then all the factors in the Japanese race are geared at a higher rate than those of the European race—are producing more of the characteristic sex-determining substances in a given time. Let us mark this difference by calling the sex-factors of the Japanese race X+ and Q+, those of the European race X— and Q—.

The cross Japanese male × European female will, as a minute's calculation will show, give female offspring with a 'strong' male and a 'weak' female factor: X+ combined with Q—. Both male and female factors are producing their determining substances; in a normal female Q keeps ahead of X in its production; but here the 'strong' X+ is producing too fast for the 'weak' Q—, and after a time catches it up. From this time forward, there is an excess of male-determining substances, and the animal must finish its growth as a male. The opposite result, when the production of female-determining substance gradually catches up and surpasses that of the male-determining, only seems to occur when a 'strong' female factor, Q+, is combined with two 'weak' male-producing factors, X— X—, and this can only come about in the second generation after a cross.

Similar reversals of sex are known in other animals, in shrimps, in frogs, and in fowls. Indeed, it is quite possible that some sexually abnormal human beings are the victims of this sex-reversing power, and deserving, not of the opprobrium which they generally receive, but of pity for being in the grip of inexorable hereditary forces.

There is one curious consequence of intersexuality. If it goes so far as to lead to complete reversal, an animal will be produced with the appearance and functions of one sex, but the chromosome-constitution proper to the other. When such an animal comes to reproduce, this must lead to upsets of the sex-ratio in the next generation. In frogs, for instance, the sex-chromosomes are XX in the female, XY in the male. When a female is converted into a functional male, she (or he, as we should now say) will still have the two X's. Therefore, when this animal mates with a normal female, which will also possess two X-chromosomes, all the sperms and eggs alike will contain an X, and all the offspring will therefore be XX in constitution, and therefore females. Such an experiment has actually been carried out, and nothing but females obtained among the seven-hundred-odd offspring.[1]

Space forbids us to enumerate more of these experiments,

[1] Precisely similar results have now been obtained by Gold-schmidt by breeding from sex-reversed moths, and by Crew by breeding from hens which had undergone sex-reversal to cocks.

for, remarkable as some of them are—for instance, the fact that if a frog which has started to lay is stopped, and the rest of the eggs fertilised three or four days later, they will all give rise to males—we have as yet no explanation for them.

We must conclude with a short consideration of sex-determination in mammals and man. As we might expect, here too sex is normally determined at the moment of fertilisation. This is shown particularly well by the fact that whenever a single fertilised egg divides so as to give rise to two or more offspring, these are always of the same sex. This occurs as a normal event in the Texas armadillo, as an exception in so-called 'identical' twins in man. Other twins, and the members of the same litter in most animals, are equally likely to be of opposite sexes.

One of the most puzzling things so far discovered about sex is that the ratio of males to females is not always equal, and may vary from species to species, and at different seasons of the year. The fact that one sex possesses two, the other one X-chromosome should inevitably produce equal numbers of males and of females. Yet in man, for instance, the ratio of male to female births is about 107 to 100, and if we take into account the embryos which die before birth, the ratio of male to female conceptions is about 130 to 100. In many breeds of animals, again, the percentage of females is greater when the breeding season is at its height, the percentage of males greater whilst fewer young are being born. Recently it has been asserted by Siegel that in man the percentage of males varies considerably according to the time during the monthly period at which fertilisation or conception takes place. If this proves to be true, the power of controlling the sex of our children, of having boys or girls at will, will be to a considerable extent within our grasp. But in face of the fact that a great many other so-called specifics for controlling sex have turned out to be worthless, it is as well to be cautious. It has been maintained, for instance, that the right ovary produces eggs giving rise to boys, the left those which give rise to girls; or that the formation of male-producing and female-producing eggs alternate, first one sort and next time the other being given off. But it has been definitely shown that there is no foundation for these and many other similar statements, and those of Siegel have already come in for very damaging criticism.

There is, however, one understood fact which may prove to explain many difficulties. As we have already seen, male mammals have but one X-chromosome. Their sperms therefore are of two kinds, one with, the other without an X. Where careful examination has been made, it is found that these two sorts of sperms can be distinguished by the microscope, those without an X being smaller.[1] It is quite possible that these smaller sperms may be less delicate, or, in their long journey to reach the ovum within the female's body, may swim at a different rate from the larger. In any case, anything which affected the two classes of sperms differently would lead to a difference in the proportion of males and females produced.

The whole problem, as will readily be seen, is far indeed from solution. But here too we have made enormous strides in the last twenty years, and instead of the vague generalities which alone were possible before, can see the main lines along which the solution is to be sought.

We can see the characters and instincts of the two sexes as two divergent possibilities of human or animal constitution, both present potentially in all individuals of the race, and only waiting the right soil to develop. From this point of view it is easy to understand the fact that has struck so many observers of human nature, that feminine characters are often latent in men, masculine in women, and in particular circumstances may emerge, to their owners' surprise and sometimes confusion. The fact of intersexuality shows us that we may have to revise not only our moral judgments but our legal practice with regard to various abnormalities of sex in human beings, and the knowledge we have acquired of the sex-chromosomes is bound in the not-too-distant future to lead to a considerable measure of control over what until recently was one of the greatest mysteries of life.

[1] In man there is a large X and a very small Y. When I visited the University of Texas in 1924, Prof. Painter demonstrated to me his beautiful preparations, which proved this fact beyond any doubt.

WHY DO MORE BOY BABIES DIE THAN GIRLS?

A FEW years ago the *Daily News* (I think it was) offered a hundred pounds for the best answer to the question, ' Why do more boy babies die than girls ? ' If I saw the winning essay, it was one of those things that one very readily forgets —about constitutional differences and innate tendencies and such-like causes which, when they are not the most general of generalities, are the mere re-christening of the facts to be explained.

If only the prize had been given a little later, and my answer could have been sent in after listening to and thinking over the papers at the British Association in 1923, I should have earned those hundred pounds ! I should have earned them with a commendable brevity; for I could have compressed my essay into two sentences: ' (1) because man has the X-Y type of sex-determination, (2) because of the existence of recessive semi-lethals and other recessive genes reducing viability.'

But perhaps the editor and his public might have liked those two sentences expounded at somewhat more length, and with less technicality.

' X-Y type of sex-determination,' then. In many, probably all, higher bi-sexual animals as well as in some bi-sexual plants, sex is normally determined by means of a difference of chromosomes between male and female.

In regard to these all-important entities, male and female often differ. In most cases, including man, the so-called XY type is found. Here, all ordinary chromosomes are present in pairs, one of each pair from the father and one from the mother: this is, in our present type, true also for the sex-determining or ' X ' chromosomes of the female. The male, however, has only one X, the other member of the pair being wholly absent, or represented by a ' Y ' chromosome unlike its mate, and usually rudimentary in size and bearing no hereditary factors.

When the time comes for forming the reproductive cells, the members of each pair of chromosomes separate. Thus every reproductive cell will possess one set or pack of the non-sex-determining chromosomes: all the eggs will have an X apiece: but of the male cells or sperms, half will have an X, the other half will have a Y (or in some species, no sex-chromosome at all). (See Figs. 2 and 3.)

What then? Put it in the form of an equation:—

$$X \text{ sperm} + X \text{ egg} = XX \text{ embryo} = \text{female.}$$
$$Y \text{ sperm} + X \text{ egg} = XY \text{ embryo} = \text{male.}$$

Somehow or other the different balance afforded by the presence of one or of two X's results in chemical differences which switch on maleness or femaleness respectively. The quantitative difference in hereditary constitution at the outset is turned into the qualitative end-result of sex-difference.

But there are numerous by-products of this mechanism; of which perhaps the most important is the fact of sex-linked inheritance.

It is clear that in the human species, all men will have received their single X from their mother, while women will have had an X apiece from either parent. (This may perhaps account for the frequency of greater likeness between mothers and sons than between fathers and sons—but that by the way.)

It is also a well-known fact that many hereditary factors are recessive—that is, do not produce their effects if masked by the presence of their corresponding dominant factor. Blue eyes are recessive to black, for instance; albinism to colour; horns in cattle to hornlessness; and so on.

But if a female is carrying a recessive character in one of her sex-chromosomes—to take an actual case, the factor for the disease known as hemophilia, or excessive bleeding due to failure of the blood to clot—and suppose she marry a normal man—what then? The result can again best be given in a diagram (and compare Fig. 3).

$$\text{Mother.} \quad \text{Father.}$$
$$\text{Parents,} \quad XX^h \times XY$$
$$\text{Eggs} \begin{cases} X & X \\ X^h & Y \end{cases} \text{Sperms.}$$
$$\text{Children,} \quad XX, \ XX^h, \ XY, \ X^hY.$$

X^h represents the chromosome with the factor for hemophilia. It will be seen that on the average half the children of either sex will possess this factor, half will be without it. But whereas in the girls the X^h will always have as partner a dominant-bearing X, and the disease will therefore never appear; in the boys the X^h if present has only the functionless, factorless Y as partner, and therefore the recessive factor can exert its effect even though present only in single dose.

Normally, therefore, the disease should appear only in males, and be transmitted to the next generation only by females who act as ' carriers '; and this is actually the case, hemophilic females being only possible as the result of a marriage between a man with the disease and a woman with one X^h.

.   .   .   .   .

We now come to the second step in the argument. It has been known for a long time that individual members of a single brood or family may show remarkable differences in vigour and vitality—in brief, in what the biologists call viability. Morgan has shown in his little fruit-fly that such differences are dependent upon mutations or changes in hereditary factors, and usually upon changes which make the altered factor recessive to the normal.

Sometimes the impairment of vitality is so great that the organism pure for these factors cannot exist at all: such factors are styled *lethals*. Or they may make it difficult for it to live in any but the most favourable circumstances—*semi-lethals*. Or merely reduce its general resistance a little—' recessive factors unfavourable to viability.'

That similarly-altered factors would exist universally is what we should naturally expect, mutations of this type simply representing more or less damage to the cogs and wheels of the machine of inheritance; and there is certain proof that they *do* exist, and in all sorts and kinds of living things, from maize to flies, from pigs to potatoes. One good example is seen in Dexter-Kerry cattle, as recently analysed by Crew. Here a lethal exists which produces a certain percentage of monstrous embryos which always die at or before full term.

What will be the consequence of the existence of such factors in the sex-chromosome? After what we have said above, it is clear that, being recessive, they will be able to exert their effect far more often in males than in females—their effect will indeed be almost exclusively masculine.

That will mean that inherent incapacity to exist, or inherent lack of resistance to any unfavourable agencies, will be commoner in males than in females, and this should hold for other mammals besides man. This is actually so, as Dr. Parkes of University College has verified. He has taken the matter a step further, since he has found that poor nutrition (in mice) not only causes more deaths of embryos *in utero* (the number dying being ascertained by the difference between the number of young born and the number of corpora lutea, or traces of discharged ova, in the ovaries)—not only this, but it causes a shift towards femaleness in the sex-ratio of the young born, a disproportionately large number of males dying as embryos.

The facts in man are all concordant. The number of males to 100 females at conception is about 130; at birth it has dropped to a little over 100 (from 103 to 107 in different nations); at 5 or 6 years the two sexes have attained equality; and by maturity the females are slightly in excess.

Furthermore, the proportion of live male children decreases somewhat with the age of the mother and with the number of her pregnancies. And the proportion of miscarriages and abortions increases with age and number of pregnancies. Thus a greater percentage of embryos die before birth in old mothers; and, owing to the existence of our unfavourable sex-linked factors, more of the excess deaths are the deaths of males.

It will be seen that the greater part of the excess of males is got rid of at or before birth, by resorption, abortion, and still-birth: what is more, of the remaining difference between the proportions at birth and at maturity, most disappears in the first year or two of life.

Now it is an interesting fact that efforts at reducing child mortality, in spite of (or because of) their great measure of success when looked at as a whole, have met with greater and greater difficulty in reducing the mortality in the first few months of life beyond a certain point; there seems, even with the best methods, to be a scarcely reducible minimum of baby deaths.

The fact that the post-natal death of males due to the existence of unfavourable factors in the hereditary make-up, is, as we have seen, most rapid in this same period, leads us to ask a pertinent question. Is not this as yet unconquered early infant mortality due, also, to the presence of such unfavourable hereditary factors in other chromosomes besides the sex-chromosome? And if so, will not the reduction of this particular section of infant mortality not merely be a task of extreme difficulty, but may it not be in some ways undesirable to reduce it? We should be simply saddling with weak constitutions the individuals whose lives were preserved, and the community with a greater proportion of unfavourable factors and unfit members. It is a point which deserves the best consideration of Public Health authorities.

Meanwhile this brief sketch will perhaps have put a number of familiar facts in a new setting, and shown on what strange and unsuspected mechanisms may hinge the most vital problems.

THE DOMINANT SEX [1]

I suppose most of us as boys and girls have been intrigued and puzzled by those passages, to be discovered not uncommonly in the most varied types of literature, which refer to the mysterious properties of Woman. Woman—with a big ' W '—so often seemed to appear to writers as a being almost wholly different from Man. She was strange, incalculable, fickle, intuitive, unplumbed; she has (indubitably!) a ' woman's heart.' . . . On the other hand, the women we knew as mothers, sisters, aunts, nurses and the rest appeared to us as perfectly natural phenomena, and indeed in many ways more comprehensible than our fathers and their masculine acquaintance.

Later on, as we grew up, the males among us began to see the force of the remarks which had so perplexed us earlier; and yet some of us may have wondered whether the girls as they grew to women did not find a precisely similar inconsequence and incomprehensibility about men? but were restrained from formulating it by reason of the contrary convention already possessing the field.

The problem is indeed an important one; for, properly understood, it involves the whole status of woman in the community. In order to form a judgment upon it, we require answers on a number of points of fact. First, is there to-day a difference between Woman and Man as finished products, and if so, how great is this difference? Secondly, granted this difference, how much of it is due to inborn differences between the sexes, how much to the different social and domestic functions of the two sexes, how much to the influence of tradition and education? And, finally, to what extent is it possible to increase or decrease the hereditary, the social, and the ' traditional ' difference? The question is thus partly biological, partly historical and anthropological—sociological if you will.

[1] *The Dominant Sex*. By Mathilde and Mathias Vaerting. Translated by E. and C. Paul. London: George Allen and Unwin.

The authors of this book have attempted an answer to the problem. Their answer, if I may try to summarise it briefly, is as follows: the biological differences between the sexes in man are negligible, so far as they have an influence upon their social status; this status is determined overwhelmingly by the ideas prevalent at the time, which in their turn help to determine much of the difference in social function between the sexes.

They document their thesis from history and anthropology. According to them, there have been, in the most various races and stages of culture, communities in which Woman has been regarded as the dominant sex, in council and administration. Once this occurs, all the rest of the commonly-received attributes of the two sexes are reversed—men are regarded as by nature coy and fond of finery, women as strong and full of initiative; and social customs and institutions fall into line with this 'reversed tradition,' women being the suitors, feminine nobles and princes keeping male harems, boy babies being regarded as a misfortune, and so forth. They adduce ancient Egypt and ancient Sparta, some tribes of North American Indians (when shall we prefer convenience to purism, and call them *Amerinds* as do the American ethnologists?), some African negroes.[1]

But, they hasten to add, out-and-out dominance of either sex is bad. Poor social status, unequal rights in marriage and divorce, economic dependence or inferiority, and, up to a certain point, prostitution—these and other evils will be found burdening whichever sex is regarded as the inferior. We therefore need a new belief and tradition, one of sex-equality, which will automatically bring about equality of social status and function between the sexes, and apparently is to minimise the biological differences as well.

There are obvious criticisms of this standpoint. In the first place, while it is true that some decades ago a considerable vogue was enjoyed by the theory that a matriarchal stage had been passed through by all or most civilisations, that belief has been more and more undermined by subsequent anthropological research. Matriarchy, or as our authors call it 'the woman's state,' was probably a sporadic

[1] An amusing satire in which this idea is developed is 'The Sacred Giraffe,' by S. de Madariaga (London, 1926).

phenomenon. Then a good deal of their evidence appears rather like special pleading. I think that scholars will need a good many more facts before they are convinced that women were truly dominant in ancient Egypt and Sparta and in the negro tribes that are mentioned.

Finally, their biological judgment is profoundly at fault. Do they, I wonder, realise that from the moment of fertilisation onwards, man and woman differ in every cell of their body in regard to the number of their chromosomes —those bodies which, for all the word's unfamiliarity, have been shown by the last decade's work to be the bearers of heredity, the determiners of our characters and qualities? Furthermore, they grossly over-estimate the ease of biological change. Of course the hereditary constitution can alter, and alter in regard to sex-difference as well as to any other character: we find degenerate females in moths, degenerate males in crustacea and worms; biologically neither sex is necessarily inferior or superior, and all grades of sexual difference from the barest minimum upwards are possible. But any considerable alteration of the hereditary constitution is an affair of millennia, not of decades.

The physical differences between the sexes in man (quite apart from those that are part of the primary sex difference) are, though not great, yet distinct enough. Size, bodily proportions, amounts of bone and of hair, voice, shape of extremities—the secondary sexual characters are perfectly definite. But let us leave these and look at the mental differences. Here recent experiment has achieved interesting results. It has shown that a male mammal after birth may be made not only in many respects physically, but also psychically female by removal of its own reproductive organs and engrafting of those of a female, and vice versa. In other words, the physical brain with which the animal is endowed is sexually neuter, blank; and in it the secretions of ovaries pick out and bring into action the nerve-paths appropriate to females, those of testes the paths appropriate to males. In man, not only does common observation as well as reasoning from lower forms indicate that this is the case, but all special investigation goes to show that the sexual feelings, whether normal or neuter or abnormal, are in the great majority of cases inborn.

The differences then are considerable; so considerable that they can never permit of the simple equivalence of the sexes. On the other hand, the superstructure of intellectual and practical life is potentially the same in both sexes. The recent Board of Education Report of the Committee on the differentiation of the Curriculum for Boys and Girls in Secondary Schools (London, 1923) has established that the intellectual differences between the sexes are very much slighter than popular belief allows. But it is temperament which in the long run decrees what we shall make of our intellects, and in temperament there is and will be—not for centuries but for biological periods—a fundamental average difference between the sexes.

This by way of criticism. On the other side of the account there is no doubt that our authors are right in emphasising how the current tradition of society may accentuate or minimise or in some points override these differences.

But I venture to prophesy not only that the inherent differences between the sexes will not tend to diminish in the course of evolution, but that man will continue, as now and in the past, to emphasise them by custom and convention.

BIOLOGY IN UTOPIA[1]

THE columns of *Nature* are not the place to discuss the literary merits of Mr. Wells's new book—although, for the matter of that, good style or artistic capacity, and appreciation are phenomena as natural as any others. Suffice it to say that he has achieved a Utopian tale which is not only interesting but also extremely readable. Most readable Utopias are in reality satires, such as *Gulliver's Travels*, and the no less immortal *Erewhon*. Mr. Wells has attempted the genuine or idealistic Utopia, after the example of Plato, Sir Thomas More, and William Morris; and, by the ingenious idea of introducing not a solitary visitor from the present, but a whole party of visitors (including some entertaining and not-at-all-disguised portraits of various living personages), has provided a good story to vivify his reflections.

However, since Mr. Wells is giving us not only a story, but his idea of what a properly-used human faculty might make of humanity in the space of a hundred generations, his romance has become a fit subject for biological dissection in these pages.

He pictures a world where, in the first place, the advance of physico-chemical science and its application, to which we are already accustomed, has attained a far higher pitch of perfection. Further, machinery has become so self-regulating that it does not make man captive, as Samuel Butler prophesied, but is a real servant. Also, instead of machinery and mechanism occupying the foremost place in the life of the majority of men, as Bergson laments that they are tending to do to-day, they have apparently been rendered not only more efficient, but more self-regulating, and are as subservient to the will of the community as is a motor-car, which never gets out of order, to its owner.

In the second place, life has been subjected to a similar control. This is a process which the biologist sees so obviously on its way that it should excite no surprise. As our knowledge

[1] A review of *Men like Gods*, by H. G. Wells. (London, New York, Toronto, and Melbourne: Cassell & Co. Ltd., 1923.)

of genetics increases, our application of it must outstrip the past achievements of empirical breeding as much as the application of scientific knowledge of principle in chemistry, say, or electricity, has outstripped the achievements of empiricism in those fields. Mr. Wells's wonderful flowers and trees are almost there already: we will not worry about them. Even his domestic-minded leopards and tigers, more ' kittenish and mild ' even than Mr. Belloc's, should not be lightly dismissed after recent experiments on the inheritance of tameness and wildness in rats.

Meanwhile, Mr. Wells also imagines a purging of the organic world. The triumphs of parasitology and the rise of ecology have set him thinking; and he believes that, given real knowledge of the life-histories and inter-relations of organisms, man could successfully proceed to wholesale elimination of a multitude of noxious bacteria, parasitic worms, insects, and carnivores. Here again we have no right to quarrel. Mr. Wells does not need to be reminded of the thistle in California or the rabbits in Australia: his Utopians proceed with exemplary precautions. All this is but an extension of what has already been begun.

In the third place, however, human as well as non-human life has been subjected to this control; and this in two ways. First, by an extension of the methods previously used. The accidents and circumstances of life have been altered—there has been a further control of external machinery. This has been, of course, chiefly in the fields of social and political institutions. A great part of such change is only intelligible as a corollary of the other supposed changes. But we may here direct attention to one idea which is imagined as at the root of much of it—the idea that man is master in his own house of Earth, as opposed to the idea which, with few exceptions, has until now dominated his history—the idea that he is the slave, sport, or servant of an arbitrary personal Power or Powers.

Finally, we come to the most radical and inevitably the most provocative of our author's imaginings—that which concerns not the alteration of things in relation to a constant human nature, but the alteration of that human nature itself. Here Mr. Wells is extremely interesting. He reduces the rôle of eugenics to a minimum, exalts that of education, or if you prefer it, environment, to a maximum.

c

Eugenic change has been restricted to ' breeding out ' (Mr. Wells does not initiate us into methods) certain temperamental qualities—habitual gloominess, petty inefficiency, excess of that ' sacrificial pity' Mr. Wells dislikes so much, and so forth.

The rest has been accomplished by proper education, and, above all, by a ' change of heart ' as regards the essential aims of life. Mr. Wells sums this up in a phrase (in which one recognises his devotion to the late headmaster of Oundle) as the substitution of the ideal of creative service for that of competition.

The realisation of this ideal is made possible in the first instance by a proper application of psychology to early life, so that painful repression and stupid suppression shall not occur, and men and women grow up unridden by hags of sex or fear, and yet without separation of any important fragment of their mental organism from the rest. Education *sensu restricto* then steps in, and enlarges the capacities of the unhampered growing mind, while the substitution of a form of telepathy for speech reduces the time and energy needed for communication. Meanwhile, a rational birth-control provides a world not overcrowded and overstrained.

By these means, Mr. Wells imagines, a race has been produced of great beauty and physical strength, great intellectual and artistic capacities, interested primarily in two things—the understanding of Nature for its own sake, and its control for the sake of humanity. By control Mr. Wells means not only utilitarian control, but that which, as in a garden, is to please and delight, and that highest control of all, artistic and scientific creation.

The Utopians, owing to their upbringing and social environment, come to think and act so that they need no central government, no law-courts, no police, no contracts. In this Mr. Wells is only telling us what we all knew already, that in most men it seems theoretically possible to produce a ' change of heart '—*i.e.* substitute new dominant ideas for old—and that if this is effected, restrictive measures gradually become unnecessary. He is careful not to make his Utopia too ideal. It is as ideal compared with this world as would be Olympus: but as little perfect as Olympus would seem to have been. The men and women there are often discontented and restless; criticism is abundant. Mr. Wells knows that intellectual and æsthetic achievement open the door to the highest known happiness of the present; he still sees that function for them in Utopia.

Let us go back and try to see how much of Mr. Wells's speculations fall within the bounds of possibility. All Utopias must suffer from lack of familiar associations, for it is by familiar associations, especially with things of youth and childhood, that emotional appeal is made and real assent gained. Thus, whatever stores of loved memories a Utopian may have, whatever driving force he may draw from the sight of familiar places and objects, we can only see his emotional life from outside, as an Englishman on his first visit to the United States notices the differences from England rather than the resemblances. But if we remember that Utopians, or Americans, must have each their private growth of life, and that this must be in many ways like ours, we get over the first stile.

We have already dealt with Mr. Wells's applied physics and chemistry and his applied biology of lower organisms. That in a sense is commonplace—commonplace made surprising; none the less, it is good to have it so well done, to have people reminded that the rate of this sort of change not only need not slow down, but can continue, and continue to be accelerated, for a very long time. What of his applied biology of man? Minor criticisms are easy to make. The Utopians, for example, go either almost naked, or else clothed in garb of the indeterminate simplicity that seems to be fashionable in all Utopias. Mr. Wells is perhaps so revolted by the dullness of modern male attire, that he under-estimates the amount by which dress enlarges the human horizon, giving us a hundred extra variations of personality, raising to an infinitude of permutations the possibilities realised in the courtship-decorations of lower animals.

With the rediscovery of Mendel's laws and their recent working out, we are introduced to the theoretical possibility of an analysis of the hereditary constitution similar to the chemist's analysis of a compound; and so, presumably, in the long run to its control. There are great technical difficulties in higher organisms, and application to man presents yet further difficulties. Still, the fact remains that the theoretical possibility exists for us to-day, and did not exist twenty-five years ago.

We must further recall the lessons of evolutionary biology. These teach us that, however ignorant we may be regarding the details of the process, life is essentially plastic and has in the past been moulded into an extraordinary variety of forms. Further, that the attributes of living things have almost all been developed in relation to the environment—even their mental attributes. There is a causal relation between the absence of X-rays in the normal environment and the absence in organisms of sense-organs capable of detecting X-rays, between the habits of lions and their fierceness, of doves and their timidity. There is, thirdly, no reason whatever to suppose that the mind of man represents the highest development possible to mind, any more than there was to suppose it of the mind of monkeys when they were the highest organisms. We must squarely recognise that, in spite of proverbs to the contrary, it is probable that ' human nature ' could be considerably changed and improved.

Next, we have the recent rise of psychology. Much nonsense doubtless masquerades under the name of psycho-analysis or ' modern ' psychology. None the less, as so shrewd a critic as the late W. H. Rivers at once saw, and as has been put to such practical uses in therapeutic treatment, there is not only something in it, but a great deal. Repression, suppression, sublimation, and the rest are realities; and we are finding out how our minds do work, ought not to work, and might be made to work. It is clear that the average mind is as distorted and stunted as a much-below-average body; and that, by just so much as a great mind is more different from an average one than great from average bodily capacity, by so much would proper training be more efficient with minds than even with bodies. Here the extravagances of some eugenists find their corrective; Mr. Wells's imagination is pursuing to its logical end the line taken by such authorities as Mr. Carr-Saunders in his *Population Problem*.

Again, Mr. Wells, being a major prophet, perceives without difficulty that the substitution of some new dominant idea for the current ideas of Commercialism, Nationalism, and Sectarianism (better not beg the question by saying *Industry, Patriotism, and Religion*) is the most needed change of all. Here, again, he is in reality only adopting the method of Lyell and Darwin—uniformitarianism—and seeking the key of the future, as of the past, in the present. There is to-day a slowly growing minority of people who not only profoundly disbelieve in the current conceptions *and valuations* of the world and human life, but also, however gropingly, are trying to put scientifically-grounded ideas in their place.

Belief is the parent of action; and so long as the majority of men refuse to believe that they need not remain the slave of the transcendental, whether in the shape of an imaginary, Being of the Absolute, or of Transcendental Morality, they cannot reap the fruits of reason. If the minority became the majority, society and all its institutions and codes would be radically altered.

Take but one example, and a current one—birth-control. When Mr. Wells's *Father Amerton* finds that it is the basis of Utopian civilisation he exclaims in horror: ' Refusing to create souls ! The *wickedness* of it ! Oh, my God !'

We are reminded of that passage in *Tristram Shandy* (ch. 21) where satire is poured on the preoccupation of the Roman Church with a similar transcendental (and wholly meaningless) problem—to wit, when could a child, as having an immortal soul to be saved, be first baptised ? Some of the suggested expedients for saving embryos from perdition prompted Sterne to inquire why all this pother could not be got over once and for all by the plan of baptising all the ' homunculi ' (*moderniter* spermatozoa) at once, slap-dash—which could be done, Mr. Shandy apprehends, '*par le moyen d'une petite canulle*,' and '*sans faire aucun tort au père*.'

. . . . .

This is the great enemy of true progress—this belief that things have been already settled for us, and the consequent result of considering proposals not on their merits, but in reference to a system of principles which is for the most part a survival from primitive civilisations.

Mr. Wells may often be disagreed with in detail: he is at least right in his premises.

A perusal of his novel in conjunction with a commentary would be useful. *Men like Gods*, taken *en sandviche* with, say, Punnett's *Mendelism*, Trotter's *Instincts of the Herd*, Thouless' *Psychology of Religion*, Carr-Saunders' *Population Problem*, Whetham on Eugenics, and a good compendium of recent psychology, would be a very wholesome employment of the scientific imagination.

THE CONTROL OF THE LIFE-CYCLE

THE control of the cycle of life in organisms is a problem of the most intricate nature, which touches not only upon the fundamentals of biology, but upon very many questions of the intensest concern to the human race. It is not in our power to give a connected account of the control of growth, for we do not yet know enough to be able to give any such account. All that can be done is to present some of the isolated views which we have been able to obtain, through the loopholes made by scientific progress, on to these hidden places of Nature, and to show what hopes this knowledge raises, but also what great need remains for organised and sustained research.

The concept of the life-cycle in higher animals involves at least six important biological processes. There is the origin of the individual's first rudiments; then growth or increase in mass; then differentiation or increase in complexity; then the maintenance of a state of balance, the condition of maturity; then senility; and, lastly, death.

The individual creature, among every group of the higher animals, starts an independent life at fertilisation, which is simply the fusion of two cells detached from particular tissues of two other animals, male and female. It begins life, not, as was supposed some century-and-a-half ago, as an immensely-reduced replica of its adult state, but as a germ, the fertilised ovum, which bears no resemblance to the adult, and is incomparably simpler in structure. Development consists partly in an increase of size, but even more essentially in an increase of complexity.

At the outset, the human individual consists only of a simple unit of living substance, or cell, a tiny round mass of protoplasm containing a nucleus and some yolk-grains, and measuring, in the human being, but $\frac{1}{125}$ of an inch in diameter.

When we set about making a machine, we draw out a plan, then construct the parts separately, and finally fit them together. The living machine which we call the body, however, is built in quite a different way; for it constructs its own plan as it goes along.

For instance, the first step in human development is the division of the germ into a great number of cells. In the next stage these cells become arranged in three layers, an outer, an inner, and a middle. This is the rough ground-plan, and is common to all animals above the level of jelly-fish, sponges, and sea-anemones. The next step forward is the formation from these layers of a much more detailed and definite ground-plan; the systems of organs are laid down.

These systems then each elaborate their own plan, the different parts of each system becoming visible; and finally these parts, or organs, become transformed, by the differentiation of their unit-cells, from mere blocks of tissue situated in their proper places in the plan, into actual working mechanisms which from now on play each their particular rôle in the upkeep and working of the animal as a whole.

To take but one example, the whole of the brain, spinal cord, and nerves constitute a single organ-system. In the very early embryo it consists simply of a hollow tube, running along the back, slightly swollen in the head, and without traces of nerve-fibres or nerve-cells. Later, the brain and its parts appear in plan, and the walls of the tube become enormously thickened, both in the brain, and in the rest of the tube, which we can now call the spinal cord. Finally, the nerves grow out from the brain and spinal cord, and enter into communication with every part of the body, forming a go-between system, allowing impressions from the outer world to be met by appropriate motions; and meanwhile the cells constituting the cord and brain became themselves totally transformed, producing a number of branching and interlacing twigs by means of which communication within the nervous system is made possible, and so, finally, association of ideas, memory, and reason.

The differentiation of the separate cells in the tissues occurs in every organ, in every tissue. In early stages the various cells are all much alike; in later stages each is characteristic. In the embryo all cells are roughly spherical or cubical, without noticeable structure. In the adult, however, we have the branched nerve-cell, the long, striated, contractile or muscle-cell, the gland-cell elaborating chemical products, the bone-cell which lays down layers of hard substance round itself, the red blood-cells—mere discs to carry oxygen —and many other distinct and differentiated types.

By this time the baby will be ready to be born. During the whole of its ante-natal period, we thus see that there has not only been an enormous increase in bulk, but also an increase in visible complexity, both in the origin of a great many different parts arranged according to a definite plan, and also in the form and arrangement of the cells which make up these parts. In other words, there has been an increase in organisation ; and this increase in organisation we call differentiation.

Once arrived at this differentiated state, the new-born baby has a long period of growth still before it, but with very little further differentiation. It is important to notice that the power of growth is progressively lost. If we measure growth not by total bulk, but by the percentage of the previous total added in a given time, we see that the growth of a child shows a continuous falling off. Minot has estimated that under two per cent. of the potentiality of growth resident in the human ovum is still present at birth; if anything, his estimate seems to be above the mark.

At length, however, he or she reaches full size, and then follows the period when neither growth nor differentiation is occurring, the adult period, or period of maturity. This lasts a number of years—many more, indeed, than those needed to attain full size—but finally (if the man has not died from disease or accident) there follows the period of old age, accompanied by loss of weight, loss of activity, loss of faculties, and this downward path at the last leads inevitably to death—to natural, as opposed to accidental, death.

In man and all the higher animals we have this cycle of existence, always proceeding in the same way; growth intertwined with differentiation at first, then growth with little or no differentiation, then maturity, a stable period without either growth or differentiation, and finally senility leading on to death.

We know that different animals have different values for these various periods. A rat, for instance, completes the whole cycle in two and a half to three years, a mouse in about two, a common white butterfly in a year, a parrot in a hundred years. Even in a single species, such as man, there are considerable variations in the rate of growth, amount of growth, and length of life; but each animal has limits set to this variation. We are given no clue by ordinary experience as to whether this type of life-cycle is fixed and unalterable for all living things, or whether there is any prospect of our being able to alter it, either by changing the rate or the length of growth, or extending the span of life.

To these questions there are two ways of getting an answer: first, by observation—by comparison of the life-cycles of all available forms of life; and, secondly, by experiment— by trying directly whether the life-cycle can be altered ' according to plan.'

Three introductory examples will, I hope, make those who are not familiar with comparative biology realise that many of the so-called ' common-sense ' views generally held about growth and age are simply held because they embody familiar facts, and are just as false as other ideas once held to be equally dictated by ' common-sense," such as the geo-centric universe or the flat earth.

The first concerns death. Weismann, the great German zoologist, towards the end of last century enunciated his doctrine of the Immortality of the Protozoa. This, for all its theological flavour, in reality embodies a simple and verifiable fact. The Protozoa are animals whose body consists but of a single cell, not of thousands or millions, like those of higher animals; they are thus all small, and some approach the original types of animal life. Paramecium is one which is often used for experiment, because of its comparatively large size (it is just visible to the naked eye), its abundance, and the ease with which it can be cultivated in infusions of hay. It is an elongated creature, covered with movable bristles by which it swims, and provided with a mouth and gullet through which it engulfs its bacterial food.

In the course of a few hours, it will grow to its full size. A constriction then appears and deepens across its centre, some of the internal organs divide, a new mouth is formed in one half, and in an hour or so separation of the halves takes place, and two paramecia are swimming about where but one was before. This is clearly a form of reproduction;

and it is by such reproduction that almost all protozoa multiply.

It is obvious that nothing has been lost in the process; there is no corpse, no new-born infant—the one old individual has simply become two new individuals.

There is evidence that this process can be repeated indefinitely. If so, it is further obvious that natural death has no chance to step in—meaning by natural death a death resulting from ageing, from inner causes, not mere accidental death through causes external to the animal. In ourselves, and all higher creatures, the growth of the body eventually must bring death; in the protozoa it never need. That is one of the penalties we have paid for our complexity.

We see also that in paramecium there is very little differentiation. In an hour or so, the dividing cell produces the parts needed; but there is never a time when we can say that paramecium is undifferentiated, in a condition like our own earliest stages.

The next example still further upsets our ideas of differentiation; for it shows that differentiation need not always proceed in the same direction, but that animals may sometimes live backwards, if I may use the phrase, as well as forward. It is the example of the sea-squirt Clavellina (p. 100), which can in unfavourable surroundings dedifferentiate, or revert to an embryonic state, and blossom out once more when times are more propitious again. In the fewest possible words, differentiation need not always go in one direction only; it may be reversible.

Our third anti-common-sense example is one with which all are perfectly acquainted; I mean the life-cycle of a butterfly—from an egg to a caterpillar, from a caterpillar to a chrysalis, and from a chrysalis to the winged, perfect insect. That transformation has been made the subject of many sermons on the topic of the life to come; but its real application is rather to this present life on earth. Familiar as is this metamorphosis, most are aware only of its external aspects; but it is the inner happenings that are really the more remarkable. Within the chrysalis shell, the active organs of the caterpillar break down into a mere pulpy mass, good only as a source of nutriment, no longer capable of living or working for themselves. The only living portions left are small scattered blocks of cells, the so-called imaginal discs, which have remained rudimentary and functionless throughout the caterpillar stage. These now absorb food from the broken-down mass of caterpillar-tissue, and eventually grow into the organs of the butterfly.

This shows us that within a single cycle of life, differentiation may take place in two entirely different directions. The same original egg turns first into the worm-like, leaf-eating, feeding-machine which we call a caterpillar, and later into a beautiful winged creature, honey-eating, active, concerned chiefly with reproduction. But the one form cannot turn *directly* into the other. The old must be broken down, and the new built from the foundations up.

What is true of bodily differentiation here is true of mental differentiation in ourselves. It often happens that a man's mind is differentiated very highly in one direction early in life, and that at a later period the same man will have acquired a quite different type of mind; but in the intervening period there will, almost without exception, have been a difficult time of transition, in which the old system was being broken down, the new built up. But that is a digression.

Let us hope that by now the reader's general ideas on growth, differentiation, and death will have been thoroughly upset. If so, we can proceed to discuss the control of growth more systematically.

In a simple but classical experiment of Hertwig's, a batch of frog's eggs was divided into four portions. One was kept at 11.5° C., one at 15°, one at 20°, and the fourth at 24° C. After three days, the first had not completed their primary ground-plan, and were still simple spheres; the last were tadpoles ready to hatch; and the other two were intermediate. It is obvious that higher temperature goes hand in hand with quicker development.

That is a practical, tangible fact. But it raises at once a philosophical problem of the most searching kind. It raises the problem, which in another form has been propounded by Professor Bergson, of the relation of time to true being.

What is the true age of these four batches of embryos? They have all been alive the same length of days, hours, and minutes. But each has accomplished a different portion of its essential cycle of being, each has penetrated a different distance along the road which leads to old age and death. Judged by outer standards, they are of the same age; judged by standards relative only to themselves, they are all of different ages. This, you will see, is the same distinction on the physiological plane that Bergson has found it necessary to carry out on the psychological plane.

To point the moral, we will take a further example, and this time one involving the end of life instead of the beginning.

As is well known, many insects live but a short time, some of them only a few weeks, or even a few days. Now this span of life, too, is a function, in the mathematical sense, of temperature. At a high temperature it is shortened, at a low temperature lengthened. For instance, Professor Loeb has investigated the duration of life of the little fruit-fly, *Drosophila* by name. At 30° C. the length of life, from hatching to dying, was 21 days; at 20° C. it was 54 days, and at 10° C. 177 days, or nearly six months. Thus the processes which lead up to and involve death are accelerated by heat. What is more, they are accelerated in a regular manner, and in essentially the same way and degree as are all ordinary chemical reactions. The rate of most chemical reactions is roughly doubled or trebled for each increase of 10° C. within the range of temperature within which life is possible; and so are the processes of life.

The fly lives more intensely at the higher temperature; but it draws proportionately nearer to its death—a situation not unlike that in Balzac's *Peau de Chagrin*.

Once more the question is raised whether age should be reckoned from the outside or from the inside. We shall have to return to that question later, and, I hope, settle it. Here we must go back to the more specific point, the action of different temperatures.

This extraordinary diversity in rate of growth or rate of ageing with different temperature, which we find in frog or fly, and indeed in all the lower animals, does not exist for man or mammal or bird. Why not? For the reason that, as regards temperature, we and these other creatures are self-regulating. We are what is popularly called warm-blooded; which really means not warm-blooded at all, but constant-temperature-blooded. Warm-blooded animals have contrived an internal temperature environment for themselves which is, within very wide limits, independent of the temperature-changes taking place in the world outside. Indeed, the development of such self-regulating mechanisms, some regulating temperature, some the chemical composition of the blood, some operating psychologically, has been one of the great achievements of evolution, and the relative independence accruing to their possessors is one of the hall-marks of a higher type.

It is thus obvious that we shall not be able to alter the rate of growth in man by altering the temperature, for the simple reason that we cannot alter the temperature.

Such failures pursue us throughout our investigation; again and again we find that in some lower animal growth or length of life can be controlled, only to discover, when we seek to apply our knowledge to man, that there stands in the way either his very complexity or the exquisiteness of his self-adjusting machinery, which resists in a most remarkable way every effort made to tamper with it.

In the higher animals, the regulation of growth is largely carried out by the organs known as the ductless glands, of which the best known are the thyroid and adrenals. The origin of our knowledge of the normal, as so often, came from a study of the abnormal; and it was through an investigation of the diseased state known as cretinism that we gained the first inkling of the functions of the thyroid.

Cretins are stunted in a particular way both in body and mind. Their condition was found to be associated with a diseased and insufficient thyroid gland. Finally, treatment with preparations of thyroid was tried, and in most cases led to the transformation to a healthy normal individual.

Many of the processes of life in cretins appear to be slowed down. This is seen, too, in the disease known as myxœdema, where the thyroid becomes diseased during maturity. In patients suffering from this, the skin becomes thick and whitish, the features heavy, and, most marked symptom of all, the mind grows distressingly slow. Here again simple restoration of the proper thyroid balance usually leads to recovered health.

Acromegaly is another curious disease. In sufferers from this, there is a progressive increase in the bony and fleshy structures of face and extremities, patients having to discard their old gloves and shoes and take to larger and larger sizes. Worst of all, the features get heavy and coarse, and the most attractive men and women are transformed into hateful caricatures of their original selves. Autopsies show that this disease is associated with a diseased and overgrown condition of the pituitary body, another ductless gland attached to the base of the brain. The very tall men, the giants of fairs and circuses, in whom the whole body shoots up abnormally in height, seem to be produced by a similar state of the pituitary, but operating earlier in life, while the bones are still growing.

By these observations it became clear that both thyroid and pituitary were in some way connected with growth. Experiment has extended our knowledge. Young dogs from which some of the pituitary has been removed grow extremely slowly, become excessively fat, and in many ways remain in an infantile stage.

Professor Arthur Keith has recently made the interesting suggestion that the differences in racial type, as seen for instance between the white, the yellow, and the black races, are due to alterations in the balance of the various glands of internal secretion. By this means, too, he seeks to explain the occasional appearance in white races of individuals of a Mongolian cast of face where no admixture of Mongolian blood can have occurred.

We shall return shortly to the question of the glands of internal secretion. Now let us for a few moments invade another field, the field of diets and food substances and their effect on growth.

As most people know by now, the established classifications of foodstuffs is into proteins, carbohydrates, fats, and mineral salts. The carbohydrates include the sugars and starches; they resemble the fats and oils in being built up out of the three elements, carbon, hydrogen, and oxygen, but differ from them in the proportions of these various elements. The proteins, on the other hand, contain nitrogen in addition to the other elements named.

As a rough analogy the human body may be compared to the engine of a motor-car. It derives its energy from the combustion of fuel, and it utilises that energy by being constructed in a special way. To keep the engine working, you must not only supply fuel, but also repair the parts as they wear out. So, too, in the body. The carbohydrates and fats are for the most part utilised simply as energy-fuel, while repair of the tissues, which are constantly in need of a small amount of renewal, is provided for by the proteins. While the animal is growing, conditions are somewhat different, for not only must the old living machinery be repaired, but new molecules continually be laid down. Up till a very few years ago, the matter had not progressed much beyond such very general notions. Now, however, we are beginning to know that that was far from all. To start with, all proteins are by no means equally good for maintenance (as simple repair is usually called) or for growth. Further, a wholly new class of food-factors has been discovered, without which growth and life itself cannot continue. These are the so-called vitamins.

It is as well to recall at the outset that nobody yet knows what a vitamin is chemically.[1] We know, however, what they do, and where they occur; and that is already a great deal. As usual, the matter has been approached by two convergent roads. In the first place, certain diseases were found, in the slow course of years, to be associated with deficiencies in diet. The best known of these is beri-beri, which was traced to its source through the observation of a Dutch doctor in Java. This was the chain of evidence:—
(1) Beri-beri was common in the asylum under his charge. (2) The fowls in the asylum yard were fed on the patients' leavings. (3) These same fowls developed a disease very like beri-beri. (4) The patients' diet consisted very largely of polished rice.

It was eventually shown quite clearly that rice from which the husk and the germ had been removed by milling and polishing was deficient in a something which was christened vitamin, and that a long-continued diet of such rice led to the development of beri-beri. Supplying the vitamin again, in any form, leads in a wonderfully short space of time to recovery.

[1] Since the above was written, rapid progress has been made in this respect, and we may soon hope to be able to state this biological problem too in terms of bio-chemistry.

This side of the matter does not concern us so much. What is of interest is the fact that it takes some time for the polished rice diet to produce the symptoms of disease. In other words, a balance is gradually upset.

It is the effect of vitamins on growth that is especially interesting to us here. Our knowledge of this chapter of biology we owe largely to Sir Gowland Hopkins, of Cambridge. He discovered that if a diet was made up of protein, carbohydrate, fat, and salts, all chemically pure, young animals—rats in this case—would not grow on it, although it contained ample substance both for energy and for repair. They not only would not grow, but soon lost weight, and died within a week or so. The addition of an apparently negligible quantity of milk, however—a mere two or three cubic centimetres a day—restored the animals to health at once.

The substance lacking in the original diet was what is now generally called fat-soluble vitamin A.

Through the vitamins we are introduced to a new class of food-factors—substances which, though absolutely necessary for growth, for health, and for continued life itself, need yet be present only in infinitesimal quantities to produce their effects. That this discovery has not been without far-reaching and important results is shown by the fact that not only beri-beri, but also other widespread diseases, like scurvy, have been shown to be caused by an analogous deficiency of diet and to be therefore preventible.

Meanwhile, other workers, notably Osborne and Mendel in America, had been investigating the properties of single pure protein substances, as tested by feeding rats and mice, both growing and mature, with them as the sole protein constituents of an otherwise adequate and ample diet. The proteins are themselves very complex substances, and are built up out of a number of less complex units, each containing nitrogen, hydrogen, carbon and oxygen, and known as amino-acids. Some proteins are deficient in some amino-acids, others in others. Some of them are correspondingly able to support life for an indefinite time, others are not.

Various most suggestive facts have emerged from the investigation. To start with, it has been shown that some proteins, such as zein from maize, will not by themselves support life at all. Many others, such as edestin from hemp, seed, though capable of maintaining a growing animal in health for a very considerable portion of its life, are yet somehow in the long run inadequate. A long period of health and growth is followed suddenly by a sharp loss of weight and premature decay, which can be arrested at once by placing the animal on a normal diet containing several proteins but otherwise leads inevitably to death. To this upsetting of the balance we shall return.

Then we have the startling fact that certain substances will suffice to keep a grown animal in health, but will not permit of growth in a young animal. Gliadin, a protein derived from wheat kernels, of which it forms about 40 per cent. of the protein content, is such a substance. Grown rats or mice fed with this not only continue active and healthy, but are capable of reproduction. Normal young rats may be born on this diet, and will grow actively as long as they are being suckled by the mother. But if, after weaning, they are continued on the same diet, growth ceases at once. Regarded as a chemical factory—as every organism can, under one aspect, be rightly regarded—the adult rat is obviously working in a different way from the young. The young animal cannot manufacture from substance which is missing from the make-up of gliadin. But once this substance has been manufactured in sufficient quantities, and growth is over, there has somehow been introduced into the organism a new bit of chemical machinery, which is capable of so transforming the gliadin as to make the missing substance not only in amounts adequate to keep the tissues in repair, but to nourish a litter of growing young, both before and after birth. That the chemical processes going on in a growing animal are different from those in the same animal when growth is over, is clearly a fact on which there hinge immense possibilities.

This property of gliadin has been utilised to produce another and remarkable result. If a half-grown animal is fed with gliadin as its sole protein, it will be able to maintain its weight, but not to add to it; it lives, but does not grow. If, however, other proteins are added to the diet, it will at once begin to grow again, and that even if the limit of the normal growth-period has been overpast. One rat was started on this late growth after 277 days of gliadin feeding and 314 days of life, and finally reached normal size; and this in spite of the fact that growth in rats is normally over at 180 days or thereabouts. What is more, the animals kept on gliadin look as old as their size, not as old as their age in days, and are indistinguishable by inspection from young normal animals of the same weight. Obviously, we next want to know whether, when the growth of such an animal is finished, its period of maturity will be as long as that of normal animals, or if its extra period of youth must be deducted from its old age. This, however, has not yet been determined one way or the other for gliadin-fed animals. From experiments, later to be mentioned, on lower animals, we know that there is at least no theoretical reason against its maturity lasting the normal period—in other words, against its usual span of life having been actually lengthened by the amount of time during which growth was stopped. But whether this be so or not, further experiment alone can decide.

Such a prolongation of life would constitute a very real positive achievement. Otherwise, these experiments, while giving us a clear insight into the conditions of growth, may all be called negative in outcome. Addition of more vitamins, of more growth-promoting proteins beyond the limit necessary for normal growth, does not result in an increase of growth. We can upset the self-regulating machinery in one direction, but not in the other.

Now let us turn to some other experiments which have achieved positive results, although this time their effect is more on differentiation than on growth. Every one is familiar with the development of the frog—how the eggs are transformed into embryos within their jelly-membranes, how these hatch into tadpoles which are to all intents and purposes fishes, breathing by gills and swimming with their tail-fins, how these grow, how from their sides there sprout out the rudiments of limbs, and how finally a sudden change, an Ovidian metamorphosis, overtakes the organism, the body-shape, and the colour alter, the tail shrivels and is absorbed into the body, the gills disappear, and the intestine, remodelling its lengthy coils into a simple loop, becomes adapted to a flesh instead of to a vegetable diet.

Development in tadpoles is a variable quantity. Food, temperature, light, and many other factors somewhat affect the rate of growth and the time of metamorphosis. Within the last ten years, however, one factor has been found which is powerful and specific in its action; that is the amount of thyroid substance present in the animal. If tadpoles are fed on ox or sheep-thyroid—and that is an experiment any one can try for themselves if they go to the butcher and get him to cut away the thyroid from either side of the wind-pipe just below the larynx—they will begin to metamorphose within a week or ten days, whatever their age. Even if no leg-rudiments are present at the start, they will appear; and the other changes follow in due course.

If the animal is too small, it will attempt the transformation but fail. There is a limit of size below which metamorphosis may be begun, but can only lead to death. However, the limit is so low that by means of thyroid, young frogs can be produced no larger than flies, and not a quarter of the bulk of those that change at the normal time.

More than this; the converse experiment has been tried, and has succeeded. Allen, in America, succeeded in removing the thyroids from young tadpoles of about a quarter of an inch in length—no mean operation ! Such animals, unless they are fed with thyroid, will never metamorphose at all, never even form legs, but continue to grow and grow into giant tadpoles double and treble the size of any found in nature: and some of these have finally been found to become almost sexually mature.

Now there exists in Mexico and the Southern United States a remarkable creature known as the Axolotl (which, by the way, is Mexican for ' play-in-the-water.' It may be added that the Mexicans eat them in quantities, stewed or fried, with plenty of cayenne pepper). This creature looks like an aquatic salamander, and lives in lakes and pools, where it breathes by gills. It closely resembles the enlarged tadpole of a newt, which differs from that of a frog in early possessing legs. Another animal of about the same size is known from the same regions, the Amblystoma. This lives on land, and is definitely a large salamander, air-breathing and finless.

In the middle of last century it was discovered that these two apparently very distinct animals were really one and the same, and that an amblystoma always started life as a little axolotl, undergoing metamorphosis later. In certain districts, however, the change never came, and the axolotls simply continued to grow and finally to become capable of reproduction in their tadpole state.

Now by means of a thyroid diet, any axolotl, no matter how large or how mature, can be turned into an amblystoma-- a transformation involving not only the disappearance of gills and tail-fin, and the growth of lungs, but also an extra growth of limbs, a change of colour, and extensive altera- tions in the skull and skeleton. On the tableland of Mexico, the amblystoma is never found, although the axolotl swarms in the lakes. Thus thyroid given to one of these axolotls turns it into a form which it has lost for thousands or tens of thousands of years.

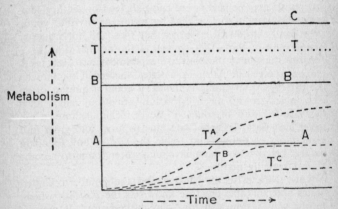

FIG. 5.—Diagram to illustrate the probable relationship of thyroid and tissues in amphibian metamorphosis. T^A, T^B, T^C, probable relative growth of thyroid in Frog tadpole, Axolotl, and Proteus respectively. A, B, and C, the threshold values (probably dependent on rate of metabolism), at which the tissues will respond to thyroid hormone. T, the maximum concentration of thyroid tolerated, is still below the tissues' threshold of sensitivity in Necturus.

But the last link in the chain remains. There are three or four other species of animals, such as Proteus, the blind 'Olm' of Carniola, and Necturus, which closely resemble the axolotl and spend a piscine existence in ponds and streams, but are not known in a land-form at all. Apparently they have found aquatic existence to pay better. In them the thyroid seems to be so reduced that they can normally never metamorphose. In others, on the contrary, the thyroid is well formed, but the tissues have lost their capacity to respond to its secretion by metamorphosis. (Fig. 5.)

These results are interesting enough in themselves, but the question remains as to *how* the thyroid accomplishes what it does. On this point, no certainty has been reached. One view may be indicated because of its bearing upon other questions. Briefly, it is this. In a developing frog the processes of growth first build up a system which we call the tadpole. Development continues, and leads, partly to the growth of this tadpole-system, but partly to the building up of a new system, the rudiments of the frog. These consist chiefly of the beginnings of lungs and limbs; but many changes in the skeleton, too, are initiated which only have meaning when looked on as forerunners of the adult state.

After a time, then, we have two systems of organs competing with each other within the single organism—the formed tadpole-system, and the forming frog-system. The action of the thyroid is, on this view, to stimulate the young, growing frog-tissues more than the older, differentiated tadpole-tissues, or, even more probably, to over-stimulate the tadpole-tissues and so give the frog-tissues more of a chance. When the thyroid has produced enough of its secretion, or when enough is introduced in the diet, the growth of the frog-system is so much accelerated that it beats the tadpole-system in the competition for food. The tadpole-tissues are in these conditions unable to maintain themselves, they break down, and become utilised as food-stuff by the remainder of the organism.

The underlying processes of life have often and justly been compared to an eddying stream; and this comparison will help us to visualise such a process. The structure of the organism can be represented by the bed of the stream; its vital processes by the flowing water. Alter one, and you alter the other. Imagine a stream flowing round an S-shaped bend, and in the second curve swirling under the bank in a broad eddy. If a little channel is dug across so as to short-circuit the second bend of the S, water will flow along this, and less will be left for the eddy. Anything which enlarges the channel will increase the flow along it, and as this increases, the eddy will lose its original character, and finally the whole of the second bend will dry up and cease to be. If the eddy in the bend represent the life animating the tadpole-system, the stream along the new cut that of the growing tissues of the adult, then if we have a workman with a spade coming and enlarging the new channel, he will represent the thyroid. That such struggling systems are not mere convenient imaginations chosen to suit the case is shown by numerous examples, two of which may be cited.

Clavellina, the sea-squirt which we have already mentioned, belongs to a group of animals which, though degenerate in that they live a sedentary life, are yet of a high order of complexity, and, as a matter of fact, are degenerate off-shoots of the ancestral vertebrate stock. Another of these, called Perophora, grows in a very plant-like way, sending out hollow shoots, full of circulating blood, from which at intervals new buds arise, so that a colony of individuals is produced with a common blood-system.

By snipping this shoot, or stolon, at two places, we isolate a system consisting of a single individual and a piece of stolon. In the laboratory it is impossible to provide the creature with the minute floating food which it finds in the sea. In spite of this, such systems, if kept in pure water, live under observation for a long time. If the water is constantly renewed, the individual continues healthy, and of the same size; but the stolon progressively shrinks, because its tissues are being used up to provide nourishment for the more highly-organised individual, which in these conditions is the dominant partner.

If, on the other hand, the system is placed in extremely dilute solutions of various poisons, we can achieve a curious result. At a certain concentration, of course, the whole system is killed. At a lesser concentration, both individual and stolon are badly affected; but a still greater dilution can be found in which the more highly-organised and therefore more sensitive individual is considerably affected, the simple stolon scarcely at all. In this case the individual shrinks, it loses its typical shape and becomes an irregular sphere, its organs collapse and become simplified, as if it were about to de-differentiate; but after a time the separate cells actually migrate out of the tissues into the blood-stream (as if a house were to unbuild itself by the bricks flying out of the walls !), and finally nothing of it is left. The stolon, meanwhile, not only keeps healthy, but may actually continue to grow at the expense of all the food-material thus provided. In fact, the boot is now on the other leg—the dominance is reversed.

The system thus consists very clearly of two lesser systems in competition with one another. When both are healthy, the most active and highly-organised wins; but this is more sensitive to unfavourable conditions, and, once affected, is unable to keep up the struggle, and is actually sucked out of existence by the other. The same sort of thing may be readily demonstrated with common hydroid polyps like Obelia.

Growth and the reverse of growth, seen in the sudden disappearance of whole systems of organs, may thus in certain cases depend on the upsetting of a balance between contending parts of an organism.

To complete our survey, we might take one further example from a very different field—that of the mind. It is well known to those who have studied nerve-disease that one set of symptoms that occurs regularly in a certain proportion of patients suffering from shell-shock and neurasthenia can be classified as *mental regression*—in other words, a going backwards to an earlier stage of mental life. Grown men behave like boys of five, lisp, forget their adult life, talk as if the memories of that early time alone were active in them, play childish games, become dependent on their nurses. In fact, they become, as nearly as their grown body permits, what they were (or what they remember to have been) at some far-past age. When this condition is carefully analysed, it is found that it, too, is the result of a competition between two systems of mind—the adult system and that of earlier times, when life was remembered as happier.

In times of severe strain, to keep the adult system going involves a constant facing and overcoming of unpleasant fact. Under these conditions its delicate adjustments are upset; the nervous energy (to use a loose but useful term) will no longer flow so readily through its channels. But nervous energy is continually welling up as a product of the activities of life; and so, being refused its proper channel, it runs into that which it finds most open to it. In some, this second channel is an imaginary world; in others it is the channel that leads to despondency and suicide; in still others it is, as we have seen, the simple revivifying of the old and less complex systems of childhood.

We seem to have wandered far afield; and yet this idea of lesser systems in competition within a greater is one of extreme importance for our problem.

Before concluding, I would like to bring up one further topic, because it so well illustrates not only the suggestiveness of our knowledge, but also reveals how great are the uncharted tracts of our ignorance.

The topic I refer to is that of cancer; cancer, which kills one woman out of every nine, one man out of every thirteen; to whose perennial ravages those of the greatest wars are nothing. Of the ultimate cause of cancer we know next to nothing. It is probable that there are many such causes. Sometimes it appears to be due to local irritation, sometimes to a poison, sometimes, again, to some ultra-microscopic germ.[1] But the end-result is always the same: some of the cells of the body become, through this or that agency, emancipated from the controlling bond which regulates the growth and harmony of the parts in the whole, and the emancipated tissue embarks upon a career of unlimited, unregulated growth and reproduction.

Let us for a moment revert to the question of growth in man or the higher animals. It should be emphasised once more how the power of growth inherent in the germ, at first enormous, decreases continuously as development proceeds.

This may be illustrated by a very simple calculation. The weight of the human germ or ovum is about $\frac{6}{10}$ths of a milligram. The weight of a new-born baby is from 3 to 4 kilograms. Thus in the nine ante-natal months the ovum increases its weight 5 or 6 million times. In the remaining 18 or 20 years of active growth, however, the child increases its weight only 15 to 20 times.

In correlation with this, we find that the power of budding and regenerating lost parts, so often seen among the lower

[1] This sentence was written in 1921. The recent discoveries of Gye, Rous, Fibiger and others seem to show that the cause of cancer is in a combination of the three causes I have mentioned.

animals, is present in the young stages of the higher types, but not in the full-grown individuals. If one chooses to take a planarian flatworm and simply cut it into bits, most of them will grow new heads and tails and become flatworms again, perfectly healthy though small. This is not possible in a newt, although even here amputated legs are produced afresh. In a lizard a new tail can still be grown, but not limbs, while in a bird or a mammal no large part can be regenerated; a limited regeneration still takes place, however, to the extent of healing-over cut surfaces.

But if, even in these higher types, we go back to the early stages of development, we find a much higher power of regeneration (and regeneration is of course bound up with the power of growth). A frog cannot replace an amputated limb: a tadpole can and does so with ease. Even in mammals this power is retained. Some ten years back, the zoological world was startled by the discovery of a Texan naturalist that the common armadillo of the southern United States reproduces partly by budding. Four young are always produced in a brood, and these all arise from a single original germ, which buds out the four rudiments of the future young armadillos after reaching the three-layered stage. In man himself there is no reasonable doubt that what we call identical twins—twins so nearly alike that confusion is possible between them—arise in a similar way by some form of budding from a single ovum, and that this common origin is the cause of their extraordinary resemblance.

But the reason that the tissues of the adult do not grow is not that they have lost all power of growth. When the muscle of an adult newt is injured, the injury can be repaired. In order to accomplish this, the muscle-cells near the point of injury lose their characteristic striated structure, which enables them to contract, and become de-differentiated. In this condition they multiply, and when enough young muscle-tissue has been produced, the new cells differentiate again, and assume the striated adult structure. It would seem as if the power of reproduction and the power of working efficiently cannot exist together in such a complicated tissue as muscle. An analogy will illustrate this. We have seen that an axolotl can be transformed into its adult state by means of thyroid. Now, if thyroid be given to a female during the egg-laying period, the egg-laying stops within a day or two, and the transformation begins. To carry on both egg-production and metamorphosis together is too great a task for the organism.

Something roughly parallel to this occurs in cancer. Each kind of cancer is produced from one particular type of tissue. In every cancer, the special structure characterising the cells of the normal tissue has been partially lost, and with it the power of working in the normal way; but meanwhile a power of growth over and above any possessed by the normal tissue has been gained, and in general, the greater the difference of the cell from the normal in appearance and working, the greater is the excess power of growth and the more malignant the cancer.

In very malignant growths, as in some spontaneous cancers of the mouse, the cancer may continue growing, like a parasite, at the expense of the animal that is both its host and its parent, and finally suck it dry, as the stolon of Perophora was sucked dry by the healthy individual. In the competition with the body, the tumour tissues, simply because they are growing, and so working faster, get first call on the available food. Some tumours take their origin from fatty tissues; these may continue to grow and to be full of fat after every fat-globule, every particle of reserve food-supply, has disappeared from the tissues of the rest of the animal. The tumour may be well nourished, the rest of the animal literally starving.

But sometimes the tables can be turned. Miss Slye has shown that if tumours are transplanted into female mice, and the affairs of these mice so regulated that they are almost continuously pregnant (as can be done by taking the new-born young away from the mother), the drain of the embryos is so great that the tumour cannot obtain enough food to grow, and only becomes dangerous when the mice are past bearing.

Nothing could better illustrate that balanced competition between parts which we have already discussed in connection with metamorphosis. It is important to note that in such a system the balance is capable of being tilted either way. Normally, the cancer wins; but if we knew how, we could o damage the cancer that the body would win, and would absorb the growth. This is what happens in successful cases of radium treatment. Occasionally, a tumour will disappear spontaneously; in such cases, too, the cancer has perhaps been damaged in some way; but it may be that the cancer has not been damaged at all, but that the body has been stimulated; for a raising of the level of the body-tissues' activities would alter the balance in exactly the same way, so far as result is concerned, as would a depression of the activities of the cancer.

Once more the bodily fact has a mental counterpart. Obsessions, complexes, and fixed ideas, whatever their origin, are always parts of the mental structure which have emancipated themselves from the proper harmony of the mind, and established themselves as dominant. They draw into themselves an undue portion of the nervous energy, and starve the other parts of the mind, finally causing a complete upset of the mental organisation and total inability to carry on its normal work.

Harmony of the parts in subordination to the needs of the whole is one of the conditions of existence for higher types of life. Cancerous growths and mental obsessions show what terrible results can follow when a part becomes insubordinate.

Enough will have been said to prove that we are beginning, however tentatively and incompletely, to gain an insight into the machinery on which the control of the life-cycle depends. Physics and chemistry, working with their simpler compounds and fewer concepts, are ahead of biology in tracing the operation of general laws in the phenomena with which they deal, and have forestalled the students of life in the construction of a cosmology. This cosmology of theirs passes, for want of others, as the doctrine of all science and as the only doctrine of science. As a matter of fact, the fullness of time is at hand in which a new and more wide-embracing cosmology can and must be enunciated.[1] The reason why this wider, more biological view of the world has not yet been promulgated is biology's own complexity. There are three lines of attack on biological problems. There is first the investigation of structures, compounds, and processes, which, though physico-chemical in essence, do not occur

[1] A notable beginning has been made with this by Professor Whitehead in his recent book, *Science and the Modern World*.

in inorganic nature—structures like the chromosomes, compounds like the proteins, processes like the immunity reactions. Then there is the investigation of these and simpler phenomena of life in the light of the principles of pure physics and chemistry. And finally there is the investigation of phenomena which are not available for study in pure physics and chemistry, nor even by the methods of those sciences—the phenomena of mind. Only when we are able to frame a cosmology which shall recognise and synthesise these three sets of phenomena, only then shall we begin to have any adequate philosophy of nature. We shall then discover that all our present definitions of matter are incomplete, and that the ' world-stuff ' is in reality endowed, not only with the properties of what we call matter to-day, but also with those of mind.

That is a philosophical digression: but it is germane to the subject, for only as knowledge progresses towards the time when such a generalisation shall be possible of acceptance by science, only so will any full measure of control be attained over the life-cycle of man, in whose workings are involved and intertwined not only physical and chemical mechanisms, of however great complexity, but mental and spiritual mechanisms as well.

The greatest event of the nineteenth century was the revolution caused by man's sudden stride to mastery over inorganic nature. The twentieth will see another such revolution, caused by another step forward in mastery, but this time mastery over organic nature. The revolution is even likely to be greater than its predecessor; for the stuff that will be controlled is the basis of our thoughts and emotions and very existence.

Are we prepared for such a change? Can we truthfully say that we have used well the power put into our hands by the discoveries of last century? Or that we are in the least likely to use well any further power such as imagination sees maturing in the womb of discovery to-day? Have our statesmen and political thinkers ever reflected on the lesson to be learnt from the past evolution of life? The future of mankind depends on two very different things—the quality of the individuals that go to make up society, and the way in which society itself is organised—its laws, its constitution, its habits and customs, its religion, its education, its organised tradition. Improvement in either is valueless in the long run unless accompanied by improvement in the other. But the evolution of the organisation of human society is in its infancy. If we were to draw a parallel between primitive types of society and some primitive mammal such as a duck-billed platypus, and to compare the course which we hope society will in time accomplish with what has actually been accomplished in the past in the progress of the mammalian type from a creature resembling a platypus to man, with what creature should we have to compare the existing state of human communities? I venture to say that we should be flattering ourselves if we were to fix upon the dog. We do not yet co-operate enough for that; our societies fall far short of any such efficiency.

But what is it which has been the determining factor in the upward progress of mammals? The answer of evolutionary history is unequivocal. It has been the increase of brain and the concomitant increase of mind. Let it be remembered that in saying this we do not commit ourselves to the view that progress has been determined solely or even mainly by increase of that part of the mind which we call intellect. An equally important factor has been the increase in harmony, in co-ordination between the parts and between the actions of the organism which, too, is dependent on the elaboration of the structure of the brain. The factors which, after once a certain modicum of physical complexity has been reached, make for survival and for progress in every type of life below the level of men, are knowledge, adaptability and internal harmony. There is no reason to suppose that these same factors are not operative in the development of the human species.

Until we devise a type of society whose traditions and institutions at least make it possible for reason to take the lead in its councils, and one which does not waste the major portion of its energy and resources in external and internal warfare—until that time we must remember that it is only we ourselves who are responsible if the gifts of power bestowed on us by the labours of the inquiring intellect are wasted, misapplied, or even turned against the very foundations of society itself.

THE MEANING OF DEATH

THAT friend of all of us, the Man in the Street, would, were he forced to reflect on such a subject as this, probably say that death was the term of every individual life—that each individuality possessed a body which grew up, aged, and finally died—and that this dying was a necessary consequence of the processes of living. This is the simple and obvious aspect of death which presents itself to one who knows only man and those animals with whom he comes into close relation—the beasts of the field, the birds of the air, and some few of the creeping things upon the earth.

But now that our knowledge of the simpler organisms, less specialised, less stereotyped in their division of labour, has become fairly extensive, it may be worth while to ask if the biologist's idea of death remains the same as that anthropomorphic one of the average man; and the writing of these lines is good evidence that it does not.

First, however, we must try to analyse further the phenomenon of death as it is seen in man. When John Brown's name appears in the Deaths column of *The Times*, what has really died—what has been lost to our world? Two things, I think we may say: first, the actual substance of his body, the protoplasm itself and all that it has given rise to—bone, gristle, hair, and the other dead things that form part of our living selves—these, though their constituent atoms persist, yet disappear as such, being gradually converted by the action of oxygen, water, and bacteria into very simple chemical compounds, or even elements: and secondly, his individuality, meaning by that not only his character and personality, but everything by reason of which he was a man and an individual man—John Brown, to be easily distinguished from all other men. For this, the Greek word Morphé has been proposed—originally, it is true, for some special cases in single-celled animals, but there is no reason why such a convenient term should not be retained to denote that Form by which any organism is to be

distinguished—the form no less of its mind and of its function-
ings than of its body.

In regard to the substance of the higher organisms there
is, in a sense, a constant death going on throughout life,
and that in two ways. First, there is the throwing off of
whole units—cells or organs—to be replaced later by new
ones of the same kind; and secondly, the continual breaking
down of the living molecules into simple waste products,
which are rejected from the body. To call this latter
phenomenon death, however, is rather a stretching of the
term, for all life that we know is as it were but the succession
of drops poised for a moment at the summit of the fountain-
jet, each one rising only to fall. The living protoplasm is
continuously building itself up out of simpler compounds,
and the energy for this it can only procure by as continuously
breaking itself down. This kind of death is part of life.
As to the casting off of replaceable units, this is death, but
complete death only for the units themselves—a very partial
death for the organism as a whole, which is something
more than the sum of all its parts. To make this partial
death clearer, let us consider what happens in the case
of a tree. Trees are in reality nothing but colonies composed
of large numbers of individuals—the shoots—each of these
shoots corresponding as regards its grade of individuality
with one of the higher animals. In the tree, however, all
these are united by a common support, the trunk, which,
formed from the tree's living substance, is yet not merely
a possession of all the separate shoots, but a part of the higher
individuality exhibited by the colony as a whole—its individuality as a tree. For I think that no one will deny that the
true morphé of the tree resides in the tree as a whole, and
not in its individual members. Now in a tree we get death
of a large proportion of these members (the flowers, for
example, each of which is only a modified shoot) every year,
and yet obviously no real death of the tree itself.

So too we must think of ourselves and the other higher
animals as being also colonies, but colonies of a lower order
—colonies of cell-individuals, while a tree is a colony of
shoot-individuals, and each of these in itself a colony of
cell-individuals. The only real difference, apart from this
one of grade, is that in the animals' predominance of the

morphé of the whole is a good deal more pronounced than in the plants; also (and the two points are doubtless correlated) the number of different kinds of shoots in a tree is very much less than the number of different kinds of cells in an animal. By looking at the matter thus we shall have no difficulty in realising how the complete death, for instance, of the cells of the skin, continuously being cast off, or of the buck's antlers, shed once a year, is such a very partial and insignificant sort of death to the whole organism, although extremely real to the units themselves. Indeed, in such a case as that of the lizard, which, by a special mechanism, breaks off its tail, to leave it wriggling in the assailant's grasp, while it escapes itself, the death of the part means life for the whole—' He who throws his tail away, Shall grow another one next day.' As a matter of fact, when the lost parts can be replaced by the whole, they are usually sacrificed to it, and their death is thus beneficial or even necessary to its life. When they cannot be replaced, their loss is, of course, injurious to the whole, but by no means equivalent to its death. A man who has lost his sight, both arms, some teeth, and a leg or so, is not dead, though his life is not so full or so complete as that of other men.

After thus disposing of this partial and beneficial death, let us come back to John Brown, and ask the question, has *all* of him died? First, has all his substance died? The answer will not be necessarily yes. For if he has had a child, it means that one of the cells of his body, becoming detached and uniting with a complementary female cell, has given rise to the whole of that child. From this it follows that these special reproductive cells can escape the death of the substance, for one of them, by continued growth and division into two, has built up the body of his son, and, included in this body, new reproductive cells for future generations. Thus there is a something which connects generation with generation by actual continuity of substance, and this something is usually known by Weismann's name of the Germ-plasm. This is potentially immortal. The parts, on the other hand, which are, in our experience, necessarily mortal in each generation form the body or Soma.

John's individuality, however, has been completely lost to the world—is altogether dead; the sole surviving parts of him are germ-cells, and they bear no impress of his morphé. They have the power (in this and in most cases, only after fertilisation, or union with another germ-cell of opposite sex) of producing or growing up into a new individual with a new morphé, but by the time they are ready to do this they have gone through a process (technically known as reduction) which makes it certain that whatever individuality, patent or latent, we may ascribe to them, is different from that of the body in which they are contained. The relation between soma, germ-plasm, and morphé is this: the germ-plasm is a continuous chain, each cell of which is produced directly from a pre-existing cell. From this chain a new soma is formed at intervals, but in the normal course of events its cells all die without descendants. The morphé can only find full expression in the developed soma, and though it is in a sense present, if but potentially, in the fertilised egg-cell from which this sprang, yet reduction and fertilisation have shuffled and recombined the cards so that even this potential individuality is not the same as that of the parent. Or, to put it in another way, in each generation the germ-plasm splits off from its immortal self a mortal part—the individual's body. From the point of view of the species the soma is but a soon-worn-out casket for keeping safe the germ-plasm's undecaying pearls—save that here the pearls make the caskets.

That is as far as we will take John Brown; perhaps I may recapitulate what we have discovered about him. First, that he has been dying all his life, but that this death is a death only of some of his component parts, and is often beneficial to him as a whole; secondly, that in what we call his death there are really two deaths woven together —death of substance and death of individuality; and thirdly, that all the substance contained in him has not died, but that we must distinguish in him a mortal, somatic part, which alone bears the stamp of a morphé, and an immortal, germinal part, not in itself differentiated, but able to produce from itself new individualities.

John Brown has kept us rather long, but at last we can turn to the rest of the animal kingdom, and see if perhaps the two deaths bound up together in man may not be found separate elsewhere. Can there be persistence of the morphé if the substance dies? In another world, perhaps, but not in this. Here we only find individuality as a function (in the mathematical sense) of a certain complexity of physical substance, as, to take a familiar if incomplete example, we only get liquid water when the temperature rises above a certain point in the scale. We cannot think of a morphé existing without substance, for, by definition, it is simply that which informs a mass of substance and differentiates it from other masses of similar substance. But we can think of substance without a morphé, and in point of fact the morphé may pass out of a mass of substance—may die—and be replaced by a new one in the selfsame mass.

Of this it will be worth while to give an example: Clavellina is the name given to a particular genus of Ascidians—creatures which are an offshoot of the Vertebrate stock. They thus stand high in the animal scale, and though degenerate morphologically, are yet much specialised in certain directions.

In order to make comprehensible what follows, it will be as well to give a short sketch of the structure of the animal. It is a sedentary marine creature, of beautiful translucency, which may reach a height of nearly two inches. In its upper part or thorax is a complex breathing and food-catching apparatus; this consists of a large sac, the walls of which are perforated by a number of little slits, the gills, arranged in rows. Water is drawn into this sac through a wide orifice that can be closed at will, and after passing through the gill-slits comes into another sac from which a second and similar orifice leads to the exterior. These two orifices are called the siphons. Numerous small blood-vessels run round and about the gills, and as the water passes through the slits, its dissolved oxygen is breathed up by the blood. At the same time the whole apparatus acts as a strainer, so that any small particles of food in the water are kept back, and accumulate at the bottom of the sac. Here they pass into the digestive apparatus, which, together with the heart and reproductive organs, occupies the basal part or abdomen of the animal. The minute nerve-ganglion lies in the thorax (Fig. 6).

Now if small individuals of this species be put in a little dish, and the water not changed, after some days they begin

to look poorly—probably as the result of starvation and
auto-intoxication combined. They shut themselves off from
the outside world by closing their siphons, and begin to
shrink. At first this shrinkage is the only noticeable change
—the organs get denser and less transparent, and all cavities
in the body decrease in volume. After a time, however, a
second process comes into play—a retrogressive development, involution instead of evolution,—in which all the
complicated organs retrace their steps, so to speak, getting
simpler and simpler, until an absolutely embryonic condition
is reached. Into the details of this interesting process I cannot
now go: suffice it to say that eventually all that remains to
be seen is a small opaque white ball, in which all signs of
activity have ceased, even the heart's action at last stopping
—its diameter five or six times less than the length of the
original Clavellina. Externally it is quite, internally almost,
undifferentiated, and bears not the remotest resemblance
to an Ascidian at all. And yet it is not dead—only asleep;
it seems that harmful influences can be better withstood when
the animal consists merely of a simple shell containing a
layer of blood-corpuscles as packing round a central bag,
than when it possesses the complicated build I have described
above. For if now put into clean water it will gradually
expand, become less opaque, grow in complexity, and finally
attain once more to the state of a fully formed and healthy
Clavellina. But it is impossible to consider the newly
regenerated morphé as identical with that which informed
the same substance before. In the first place, the new creature
is smaller than the original; this, if course, is in itself not
very important, and is largely to be explained by the fact
that the animal has had to feed upon itself to supply energy
for the complicated processes which it has performed. But
then, in the second place, the proportion of the different
divisions of the body to each other has been altered; and
thirdly, the number of rows of gill-slits and the number of
gill-slits in each row is different. Thus the morphé, which
disappeared as such when the animal returned to an undifferentiated state, has not come back again; it is gone,
it is dead, and a new morphé has arisen in the identical
mass of protoplasm. The animal has no longer the same
individuality as at the beginning of the experiment.

A very similar process often occurs in the single-celled Protozoa: when exposed to unfavourable conditions the animal shrinks slightly, loses all its typical shape and organs, and becomes a mere ball of protoplasm, at the same time surrounding itself with a resistant wall, thus becoming what is called a cyst. If its surroundings grow more congenial, it will hatch out of this, develop the morphé typical of the species, and go on with life in the usual way. In many cases, we know that all the most characteristic organs of the body—the minute but often complicated oars and paddles, traps and mills—are cast off before encystment, so that here too the morphé has not merely been latent in the undifferentiated cyst, but has died, and a new one has been born to take its place.

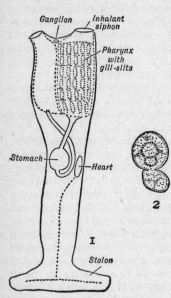

FIG. 6.—De-differentiation in Clavellina.

Diagram of the structure of a normal individual; (2) the same individual in the de-differentiated state. From this state it may recover and once more attain to full functional complexity.

In these two cases, what really happens is that the whole of the substance goes back to an embryonic, unspecialised condition in which it can be compared to germ-plasm. It is as if John Brown on his death-bed were to have his tissues pass into a state of flux, and then get simpler and simpler, until you would have to say, This is no longer a man, but merely a mass of man's protoplasm; and as if finally this mass were to re-differentiate up again—into John Brown, junior, with an individuality as obviously new as if he had arisen in the usual way, from one undifferentiated cell instead of many.

This discussion leads us on to the question whether death is a necessary consequence of life? For if we could take a Clavellina, and after making it go through the process I have described, let it grow to its original size, and then begin again *da capo*, there seems no reason (though the experiment has not been tried) why the same substance should not go on for ever producing new individualities out of itself. In parenthesis it may be said that cases like this of Clavellina show that Weismann's doctrine of rigidly separate soma and germ-plasm cannot be upheld in all its strictness. The separation is usual, but not necessary.

The important new fact which we learn from the behaviour of Clavellina is really this: that the cells which have been specialised to perform all the diverse functions of its body can revert to a primitive, embryonic state, capable of new growth and new specialisation, often in new directions. That is to say, their having been employed in some definite capacity by the soma has not impaired their other capacities— or, in other words, active and specialised function does not of necessity lead to the death of the functioning substance.

Here perhaps is the place to consider Weismann's well-known view of the immortality of the unicellular organisms. These, of course, multiply typically by dividing into two, each half often resembling its parent in every respect save that of size. Probably in all cases, in many certainly, death of the old morphé and birth of two new ones is involved in this. As a very good example we may take a form such as Euplotes (a hypotrichous infusorian) in which the organs are highly differentiated, and the process therefore easier to follow. In this microscopic creature there are various hooks and hairs and bristles grouped over the body in a definite arrangement. On morphological grounds they are all considered to be modifications of cilia, the little motile hairs by means of which many protozoa swim. When a Euplotes divides, a constriction appears round its middle, which deepens and deepens until it at length cuts the body in two. Meanwhile, all the old organs are reabsorbed into the body, and in a corner of each of the daughter-individuals appears a little patch of motile cilia, corresponding in number, but not at all in shape or position, to the various bristles and hooks in the adult animal. As the process goes on, these gradually enlarge, get stiff, and differentiate into their definitive forms, meanwhile arranging themselves over the body in such a way that each daughter finally becomes a Euplotes of the normal type. Here it is evident that the parent's morphé is dead and gone, and that two new ones have been born in the two offspring—we can see it happen.

This birth and death of individualities Weismann of course admits; what he insists on is the absence of what we are accustomed to look on as true or total death—death of the substance. As he tersely puts it, there is no corpse. Now in one large group of the Protozoa—the Infusoria—after a long period of reproduction by this simple splitting, there occurs a sexual process between two individuals, called conjugation. Moreover, the nucleus (that part of the cell which seems to be in chief command) is in the infusoria differentiated into two parts—a large macronucleus, which regulates the general vegetative life of the cell, and a small micronucleus, which usually remains quite passive. These may be considered as somatic and germinal respectively, for at the time of conjugation the macronucleus breaks up and degenerates, while the micronucleus, after engaging in an interchange of substance—a primitive sexual act—with the micronucleus of the other conjugating infusorian, divides into two halves, one of which enlarges to form the macronucleus of the next cycle of ordinary division, the other remaining as the immortal germ-plasm of the race. It was urged by Weismann's opponents that in the process of conjugation Death did step in, claiming the substance of the macronucleus for himself. Upon which Weismann retorted that they might if they liked say this was a form of death, but that there was nothing you could call a corpse, and so it was but a partial death, comparable only to the partial death of higher animals when they throw off and replace an antler or a layer of skin. However, in this case I think the opponents are in the right, as we may see if we keep two points in mind—the one Weismann's own idea of the distinction between soma and germ-plasm, the other the fact that in any cell we may compare the nucleus to the designer and builder, the rest of the protoplasm, or cytoplasm, as it is called, to the bricks, the raw material with which he builds; both are equally necessary for the completed edifice, but the nucleus is the active creative component.

On a previous page we compared the soma of man to a casket for the safe-keeping of the germ-plasm; let us change the metaphor, and extend it to cover the whole animal kingdom, by saying that Soma is the active partner and Germ-plasm the sleeping partner in the firm of Life. The active partner does all the work, but has to share the profits with his colleague. To make the parallel exact, we must simply suppose that Soma usually gets worn out with his hard work, and that then Germ-plasm can keep the firm going by producing (out of himself) a new active partner, relapsing then once more into his sleep. If we take this comparison to guide us, we shall see that in the Infusoria it is the macro-nucleus who is the active partner in the firm; he it is who works on the raw material of the cytoplasm to keep the everyday life of the animal agoing. As the whole creature is but a single cell, its cytoplasm must always persist to form a protective case for the nuclei within. But at conjuga-tion, though this survives, yet all the directive force of the soma and the whole somatic life perishes in the old macro-nucleus, to be re-created in a new one that the micronucleus is to make. Thus in the decay of a many-celled animal's body and the casting out of a single-celled infusorian's macronucleus we see the same essential fact—the death of the directive portion of the soma. It is only a difference of degree that in the one case the mortal is much larger than the immortal, and has been playing the part of protector, of sheltering home to it, while in the other that which survives incloses that which dies, and is larger and more conspicuous than it. In both, what survives is the minimum which can perpetuate the race.

Among the Protozoa, this somatic death is seen most clearly in the Infusoria, but all other members of the group probably show it in some form or another. Bacteria, it is quite possible, go through no such process: in those that do not form spores we should then have a real absence of death. However, their small size has so far precluded much investigation on the point, and they cannot yet be taken as proof on one side or the other. Thus the unicellular organisms (leaving the doubtful Bacteria out of account) do not in their normal processes lend much colour to the view that death is but an accident, and all protoplasm, however functioning, potentially immortal.

On the other hand, recent workers have experimentally shown that Infusoria may be bred through a very large number of generations indeed without conjugation (and therefore without death). This they have done by feeding them on a different diet day by day, or, when they appeared poorly (often a preliminary to conjugation), by providing various chemical or physical stimuli, adding beef-tea to their water, for instance, or taking them on a railway journey to give them a good shaking-up.

These experiments (discontinued only after hundreds of generations, when it seemed clear they might be made to go on for ever) seem to show that functioning protoplasm is not in itself mortal, but that the cause of death is to be found among the external conditions; for by altering these death may be put off, it would seem, indefinitely. In this particular case, it appears that the long-continued action of one set of conditions may so to speak push the protoplasm, always in one direction, until at last its equilibrium is upset, and death sets in unless the little-modified germ-plasm, which has not had to contend with the outside world, is woken from its sleep to readjust the balance.

There are other instances, both among animals and plants, which confirm us in this view. To take the animals first, we find that in many species of ascidians related to Clavellina, there is, in addition to ordinary sexual reproduction, an asexual reproduction by budding. In some cases the buds arise directly from actively functioning parts of the oganism; the cells at one point lose their specialised character, take on the general appearance that we associate with embryonic tissue, and then, growing and multiplying rapidly, give rise to the rudiment of the new individual. It is not yet known if this budding process can be repeated indefinitely by the same mass of substance—usually the stock dies down in the bad season of the year—but from what we do know it seems at least probable that in favourable conditions it could go on without fixed term.

This case is like that of Clavellina, except that here only a part of the tissues actually working in the service of the body passes back into an embryonic state and regenerates an active whole. There are other examples in animals, but all exhibit the same features: although actively functioning substance may continue producing new individuals, yet it always goes back first to an undifferentiated state, the old morphé dies, and with it often a large part of the old substance as well.

When we come to plants, our case is clearer. First we have the records of trees of vast age and size, whose death seems only to have been due to accident; that is to say, to something in the external world and not in the tree itself, and something which could be avoided. Such a one was the huge Dragon-tree of the Canary Islands; discovered in the fifteenth century, it impressed the Spanish explorers with its enormous bulk, and even then had a great hollow in its trunk, eaten out by winds and waters. Blown down at last by a tempest in 1868, its age must have been several thousand years—several thousand years, be it remembered, of continuous growth. Then there was an enormous Baobab at Cape de Verde, whose age a French naturalist calculated from the number of annual rings of wood to be over five thousand years. Ages which must be measured thus, in thousands of years, are attained fairly frequently by certain other kinds of trees, such as the Cedar and the Sequoia gigantea or Big Tree of California. Now if we consider the conditions to which a tree like this is subjected, we shall wonder more and more at its reaching such an age in a state of nature. Prolonged drought may cripple it, lightning may split it, swarms of caterpillars devour its leaves, hordes of beetles ruin the young shoots, fungi corrupt its bark. A single hole in this protective sheath will let in corroding air and rain to eat out great hollows in the living wood beneath. Then comes a great storm—the tree could have weathered it before, but now the weakened trunk gives way—and all is over.

One injury inflicted leaves the tree weaker and so more liable to others, and makes it possible for influences that would have been harmless before to act injuriously. The wind that blew the tree down would have been powerless if it had not been for the hollow trunk; this could never have been eaten out but for the hole in the bark, which

again was only there because of the attacks of parasites.
Of this a curious but apposite instance may be given. In
the Forest of Compiègne there is now a rifle-range down
one of the great rides; it is almost exclusively near the butts
of this range that the trees are infested with Longicorn
beetles; and the cause of this is—bad marksmanship! The
trees here have been pierced with bullets, and their wounds
have in the first place lowered their general vitality, so
attracting the female Longicorns who always prefer to lay
their eggs on weakly trees, and secondly provided an actual
passage making it easier for the larvae to reach their chosen
home just below the bark. These larvae are very destructive,
so that the bullet-wounds not only weaken the tree directly,
but betray it into the hands of new and otherwise powerless
enemies. It is a geometrical, not an arithmetical progression
of disasters. But the disasters are usually few and far between.
Great droughts, or tempests, or floods do not come every
day; and it is these great exceptions that do the tree more
harm than all the times between. The tree with but a few
short centuries of life will have to weather only one or
two; but in five thousand years there is time and to spare
for every sort and kind of thing to happen. And so, owing
to the rarity of disasters and cumulative effect of injuries,
the long-lived tree is, *ceteris paribus*, less favourably conditioned than the short-lived. To be Irish, the longer it
lives, the sooner it ought to die.

Thus it is nothing inherent in the tree itself that causes
its death, merely the long-continued shocks and buffets
of the world, preventable things, one and all; by which
I mean that if one could shelter the tree from storms, keep
off its active enemies, and provide it with a reasonable and
constant supply of food, water, and air, we must suppose
that it would go on living for ever.

This is very clearly brought out where man has actually
stepped in. It will perhaps come as a shock to hear that
there is only one particular double cherry in the world;
but that is in a certain and a quite real sense the truth.
The double cherry has no organs for reproducing itself
by seed—they have all been converted into petals; and
it depends entirely on grafting for its continued existence.
Here we have proof positive that death in a double cherry-

tree is due merely to the accumulated effects of harmful influences acting on the parts which have been long exposed to them; for if we take a young shoot from an old tree and graft it on to a suitable stock, it will grow rapidly and form a new tree in itself.

Still better are those cases where the plant is propagated by cuttings, for here we have not got to call in an individual of another species to act as a stock for the graft. Many cultivated plants are grown exclusively in this way. A very good instance is the Italian Poplar; this is a variety of the Black Poplar, differing from it chiefly in its pyramidal shape, caused by the branches growing upwards instead of outwards. It is now found all through Central Europe, having been much planted along roadsides. The curious fact about it is that only male trees are known. It can thus of course never be grown from seed, and is as a matter of fact propagated entirely by cuttings. Here again we see that at the death of the tree, the young twigs only die because the older parts are worn out by their long struggle with adverse forces and can no longer support the younger. If the young shoots are cut off and put in the ground, they will continue to live and grow, with no loss of their morphé, and the process may be repeated, so far as we know, indefinitely.

Take yet a third case, where man has not to interfere at all with the tree itself, but merely takes care of it and keeps it safe from enemies. The famous Banyan-tree of India sends down vertical shoots from its branches which take root when they strike the ground, so that a colony of Banyans is formed, each one connected with every other. In the Calcutta Botanical Gardens is one of which great care has been taken: the young hanging roots are each ensheathed in a bamboo tube till they are safely fixed in the ground, and all goats and cattle are kept away. A growth unparalleled before has been the result: the tree now covers more than two acres of ground, and shows no sign of flagging in its formation of new trunks. This is an excellent instance of what may be done by artificially repressing the harmful influences that would be at work in a state of nature.

Having thus persuaded ourselves that a single individuality can in some cases go on living indefinitely, two pertinent questions arise and demand an answer. First, if functioning protoplasm is not necessarily subject to death, why did death appear? And by death I do not of course mean accidental death, whether by enemies, parasites, or the violence of inorganic nature; but natural death, best seen in man and his domestic animals, which, although much better protected from foes and harmful influences than wild creatures, yet always visibly grow old at last, lose their faculties one by one, and pass away by a death which is a mere failure to live. And our second question is, granted that death must come, will it be possible, in ourselves for instance, to postpone his coming—for a short space—for a long space—or even for ever? It will help us in answering the first question if we make a comparison of the average length of life in various animals of the same group. We shall find that though in a rough way long life is associated with large size, yet there are very many exceptions; to take but one, the parrot lives from fifty to a hundred years, while the far larger ostrich never exceeds fifty, and rarely reaches forty. With what then does length of life stand in relation, and how is it regulated? We begin to see light if we bring in another fact—namely, that the numbers of any species remain on the whole very constant, though the number of eggs or young is always much larger than that of their parents. Thus out of all the children of every pair, only two can on the average survive to maturity, or the numbers of the species would not remain constant. Even to rear these two is a struggle, and the most direct means to this end—the perpetuation of the race—(as opposed to those attributes which help the individuals within the race to survive) are, first, large number of offspring, to utilise every possible chance; then, quick growth and early maturity, which means that generation more rapidly succeeds generation; and thirdly, long life, which makes it possible for one pair to have many broods. The product of number of broods into number of offspring at each brood into quickness of growth, divided by the mortality of the offspring, is a constant. These three factors, like any other attributes of the animal, can be altered by means of natural selection. The details will vary in every case; now length of life, now increase of progeny, will be most suitable to work with. In birds, for instance, long life has in general been favoured: a large brood would be harmful, as the weight of the eggs within the mother's body would be so great as to render quick flight impossible.

As was pointed out for the giant trees, the ill effects of external nature have a cumulative action as time goes on; and so for a species normally to have a long life means that it must be guarded effectively against this accumulation of evil influences. This could be accomplished by natural selection favouring those individuals with the most stable constitutions and the best protections against external foes; but the difficulty of prolonging life for a year would become greater with every year added, in much the same way that the horse-power of a fast liner must be disproportionately increased to add a single knot to her speed. Thus it is that no known animal reckons its life in thousands of years, and but few in hundreds. From the point of view of the species it is less simple to go on living (I speak teleologically, but my words can all be translated in terms of natural selection) than to abandon the old battered body, whose repairs cost so much time and trouble, and grow a new one from the germ-plasm.

So this increasing difficulty of repairing any damage to the body gives us a reason for the origin of death: natural selection *could* no doubt prolong the span of life, but after a certain time it comes cheaper and easier to rely upon a new life for perpetuating the species. Thus the old life, no longer nicely adjusted by selection, is at the mercy of any harmful influences, and in a state of nature soon succumbs.

This leads naturally to our second question, for surely we may suppose that if death can be postponed by natural selection, it can be also by artificial selection. The case of the Banyan-tree shows what a very limited amount of care will sometimes do. But in ourselves, the problem is more difficult, for our senescence seems at first sight due much more to internal than external causes.

Metschnikoff devoted much time to the attempt to analyse these causes. One thing at least he has made probable— namely, that natural death is very rare in organisms; but that when it does occur in man it is in truth natural, in the sense that it is as desired and almost as painless as sleep.

He holds out the hope that by healthy living we might confer upon the majority of men a happy old age and a natural dying. On the other hand, his speculations on the rôle of intestinal putrefaction in inciting the white blood-corpuscles to attack the brain cells in old age have not stood the test of time very well.

Later workers have been more successful. Steinach, Sand, and Voronoff have accomplished much towards achieving a successful practice of rejuvenation, by methods concerning the ductless glands. These wear out in old age, like the rest of the tissues. If they could be caused to become active again, the tissues would again be tuned up to their proper pitch. Practice is based upon the view that stimulation of one ductless gland will react beneficially upon the rest. Since the hormone-producing part of the testis is the most accessible, this has generally been made the starting-point. By ligaturing the duct of the testis, Steinach was able to rejuvenate ageing rats. By repeating the process first on one testis, then on the other, and finally grafting in testis from a young animal, he was able to effect rejuvenation three successive times in one beast.

Voronoff has worked mainly on human beings, with a special technique of grafting. His case-books make interesting reading. One is scientifically impressed, if not morally edified, by the record of one patient who, after successful rejuvenation, began leading a very gay life. To his friends' remonstrances he replied, ' What matter ? I can always go to Voronoff again.' And go he did, when the collapse came; and again had his clock of life successfully set back.

There are, however, some facts which make it clear that rejuvenation cannot be repeated *ad libitum*. Each time Steinach's thrice-rejuvenated rat fell into senility, it did so quicker than the time before. Some tissues like those of the nervous system probably age irreversibly, and are given but a temporary fillip by the fresh hormones.

We know, too, that the connective tissue of a chicken cultivated outside the body can go on multiplying at the same rate years after it would have died had it been left to form part of a fowl; so that there is something in the organism which limits the length of life, but is absent from some at least of its component parts.

In conclusion, it should be recollected that longevity is clearly in part inheritable. In lower animals we can demonstrate that there exist Mendelian factors which alter the average duration of life; and there is no doubt that this holds good also for man. By eugenic measures we could unquestionably raise the average span of human life, even without further progress in hygiene.

In this essay we have touched on many speculations. One thing emerges as certain: that if, as we may confidently predict, the present trend of affairs continues, more and more men will attain an advanced age, whether naturally or by rejuvenation; the death-rate of infants and young people will continue to fall; the birth-rate will continue to fall also; and as a result we shall in a few decades have a population in which the relative numbers of young and old people will be quite different from the present. By that time perhaps we shall not be quite so casual about human biology as we are to-day, and will not permit any one, even persons diseased or in receipt of relief from the community, to have as many children as they choose, or allow all and sundry to be rejuvenated, any more than to-day we permit persons to drive where they like in the roadway, or to go about while capable of spreading infection. But that is to stray from death to life, and from pure to applied biology.

'ELIXIR VITAE'

Elixir Vitae. . . . The mediæval alchemists concocted their potable gold with a strange mixture of magic and science and sought to manufacture the liquid whose draught should stave off death. The echo of their efforts still sounded; elixir, that Arabian word, still lingered on, but only in the hyperboles of the minor poet or the puffer of patent medicines. Now, however, in the twentieth century, we are presented with it, fully accredited, from that unexceptionably businesslike spot, Chicago.

It has been found possible to prolong the life of an animal for many times its usual span; and indeed there is no reason to doubt that this prolongation could be made indefinite, and that the same individual could be made to continue so long as life was possible upon this earth.

Elixir vitae. . . . Is then the alchemists' dream come true? Hardly in full, one is compelled to admit: for it is so far only applicable to a particular branch of that somewhat lowly group of the animal kingdom known as the Platyhelminthes or flat-worms. None the less, the experiment is a notable feat on the part of its author, Professor Child, of the University of Chicago, for it and kindred work have gone far to clarify our ideas on the process of ageing, which clarification, as the most impatient would-be Methuselah would admit, is best begun on simple forms of life.

It has been known for some time that these flat-worms —creeping fresh-water animals of half an inch or an inch in length—possessed the remarkable power of living on themselves when starved. We ourselves have the same power, but in a very limited degree; after a few weeks at the most, we exhaust our reserves and we succumb. But the flat-worm can cut its coat according to its cloth. Like a man who, after a reverse of fortune, sells half his possession and continues life on a more modest scale, the starved worm continually decreases in size, at the same time utilising the material which it abstracts from its own living tissues as food for the diminished whole. Death only comes with months of starvation, and not until the creature has reached an almost microscopic size, less than that which it possessed when it hatched from its egg.

This is remarkable enough; but perhaps more so is the fact that as it grows smaller, the adult shape and proportions give place to those characteristic of young worms. This had been investigated some twenty years ago by another Chicago man, Professor Lillie. Child took up the problem and showed that in physiology and behaviour too the worms made small by starvation resembled normal young ones. From this it was natural to conclude that starvation made the creatures young again in the full sense of the word.

Accordingly a family of worms was divided into two lots: one lot was well supplied with food, the other alternately starved and fed and so kept within definite limits of size. The experiment was continued for a time that permitted the first lot to pass through nineteen generations —a time which in human terms would take us back into the Middle Ages, a century or two before Christopher Columbus and his voyage. During the whole of this period the worms of the other lot remained within the same narrow limits of size, and what is more, showed no signs of senescence.

FIG. 7.—Outline scale drawings of (1) a full-grown Planarian worm, and (2) the same animal after prolonged fasting.

They had been kept within the same limits of age for nineteen generations of time. And if any one were willing to take the trouble, there is no doubt whatever that they could be so kept for ninety generations or nine thousand.

So was achieved the experimental proof that, although age in ourselves and other animals is a matter of fact bound up with the passage of time, yet this is secondary, not inherent in the nature of things. To grow old means to change internally in a particular way, not to have lived so many months or years; it is Life, and not Time, that brings Age.

BIRTH CONTROL

THE Battersea and Stepney local Health Authorities have recently applied to the Ministry of Health for permission to give information and practical advice about birth control. The Ministry has replied that if they do so, their grants will be discontinued. Much the same thing has happened in North Kensington. The first decisions were taken before the advent of the present Government to power, but the same policy still appears to remain in force.[1]

This is in democratic England in A.D. 1924, not under a theocracy enforcing its own canons of morality, nor yet a military autocracy determined at all costs on cannon-fodder.

I wonder very much what are the grounds for this attitude. There exist, so far as I am aware, two kinds of argument against birth control. The first is the nationalists', who see in birth control something which will gradually dry up the sources of population and leave the country behind in the race with more procreative nations. The second is that of the Church—officially so of the Roman Catholic Church, unofficially (though some change is of recent years apparent) that of the bulk of the ministers of other Churches. It is the moral argument: remove the check provided by the thought of 'consequences' in the shape of another mouth to feed, and the population will plunge into sexual excess. The strict Catholic goes further, and says that it is unjustifiable human interference with the number of souls divinely ordained to be brought into the world: but with that type of argument a secular civilisation need hardly feel itself called upon to contend.

There are naturally a number of variations upon each of these themes, but the themes remain the same. The one concerns itself with population—the physical results; the other with morality—the spiritual results.

.   .   .   .   .

Let us look for a moment at some of the facts. A walk round Cambridge Circus or Leicester Square or one of a

[1] This was written while the Labour Government was in power.

hundred other city streets will convince any one who will keep his eyes open that the Ministry's refusal is not part of a coherent policy. If it is really undesirable to spread the knowledge and practice of birth control, why not (it would be quite simple) forbid the sale of contraceptives and contraceptive literature, instead of allowing them to flaunt themselves in the present mean and dirty way? The Ministry's action simply makes it more difficult for the poor, the timid, and the modest to practise birth control, while the rich and less squeamish do so already.

But there is a further and more serious aspect of the situation. One of the most salient facts about recent population statistics is the rapid drop in the birth-rate within the last century. This has been very marked in the ' upper classes,' especially in families of professional men and intellectuals, less so among skilled, much less among unskilled labourers, least so in the slums. This has undoubtedly been brought about chiefly by the practice of contraception. Its result, although certainly not so serious as writers like Dean Inge and Professor MacBride seem to think it, is none the less certainly dysgenic : the better elements in the population are, on the whole, multiplying less rapidly than the less desirable.

These two facts alone seem to me to knock the bottom wholly and completely out of the population argument. Birth control *is* being practised, and it is being practised more by the classes carrying better hereditary factors than by the less favoured sections of the population. The present situation is wholly bad. It can be remedied in two ways— by a total suppression of contraception, or through its equal practice by all classes. The former is utterly impracticable. Remains the second, and the Ministry of Health is doing its best to prevent that.

But there is still another point. Within wide limits, a decreased birth-rate is largely compensated for by a decreased death-rate. Further, when children come like rabbits, not merely is infantile mortality high, but there is not enough money for adequate food or clothes, not enough time for care—and the quality suffers. Quantity of population versus quality of individuals—who would hesitate?

A page from the book of one of the voluntary birth control clinics, to which, mostly with doubts and timidity, mostly, too, with the approval of their husbands, working women come:

' Mrs. A., aged 44; 12 children born; 5 miscarriages, brought on deliberately.

Mrs. B., aged 38; 12 children born; 1 miscarriage; now pregnant again.

Mrs. C., aged 31; 7 children born—1 dead; continuous backache.

Mrs. X., aged 23; 5 children—3 dead.

The weekly wages earned by the husbands of these women are between £1, 10s. and £2, 10s. 6d.'

It is here that we are brought up against the moral argument. Shocked hands are raised, and the ' lower classes ' are told that if they could only exercise more self-restraint they would not only lay up righteousness unto themselves, but also be spared these inconvenient consequences. When, however, the argument is examined, it is seen to be no argument at all, but partly a confusion of thought, partly a conclusion from a false premise.

It is a confusion of thought because self-restraint would still be a virtue—nay, more of a virtue—if birth control were habitual; and it is, by many of its upholders at least, based on the premise that sexual pleasure is in itself in some way wrong and degrading unless associated with the deliberate purpose of procreation.

This is a difficult subject to discuss, but it is the tacit assumptions held by so many people on this very point which stand in the way of advance. ' Profane love ' is in no way wrong nor degraded in itself; but, just because it is so deeply rooted in us, so intimate, and so overwhelming, there is still a taboo upon it. All the important activities of life have had their taboos at one time or another, and sex is the last of the great taboos.

How horrified was Blake at this attitude. He shrinks in incomprehension and dislike from those who make a practice

' Of calling that a hateful thing
On which the soul unfolds her wing.'

There are, of course, those who tell us that we should eat only to live and not enjoy our food. But the sooner this attitude to any of the natural activities of man is recognised as a mental disease the better.

If the Church as a whole opposes birth control, she will be making another of those mistakes which seem inevitable to religious organisations, and are repeated with great regularity as occasion offers—it will be opposing an instrument of possible progress on the ground that it is immoral. Almost every great extension of man's thought has been opposed as a Promethean presumption. We have not to go back to Galileo or Giordano Bruno. There are those living who remember the obloquy heaped on the Darwinians, and we have only to cross the Atlantic to see that spirit in action in the person of Mr. Bryan and the Fundamentalists.

With purely material inventions the opposition has not been so frequent, but when it comes to biological inventions —inventions which affect us personally and emotionally, as organisms—we find, as Mr. Haldane has pointed out in his amusing and stimulating little book *Daedalus*, that matters are very different. The invention of alcohol has brought the fanaticism of prohibition; vaccination has its conscientious objectors, and out of bacteriology has grown anti-vivisection. When the use of chloroform was introduced, there were religious moralists who disapproved of its employment in childbirth, as circumventing the Divine Curse on women ! There are even in the United States many denominational colleges where the professors may not smoke. And now we have birth control—one of the very few big biological inventions yet made.

If people and Churches would only remember that the gifts of nature and the works of man are only good or bad as we make good use or bad use of them !

Luckily, however, if we are to judge by the recent ' Copec ' discussions, there are now signs of a really scientific temper being displayed on such questions by a considerable body of Churchmen.

A rational birth control would right the balance which the differential birth-rate is upsetting; it would give a chance of a reasonable existence to millions of women, whose lives are now made a burden to them by a succession of confinements breaking in on an unending round of domestic overwork; it would improve the physique of the children and give them a better chance in life; and it would slow down the rate of our multiplication so that we might hope that our schemes for social improvement would begin to catch up with the problems with which population increase is always presenting us.

Meanwhile the Ministry of Health makes the worst of a bad business by an aggravating and futile ruling. And this a Labour Government ![1]

[1] Note (1926). No change yet observed with the Conservative Government!

THOMAS HENRY HUXLEY AND RELIGION [1]

' So far as the laws of conduct are determined by the intellect, I apprehend that they belong to science, and to that part of science which is called morality. But the engagement of the affections in favour of that particular kind of conduct which we call good, seems to me to be something quite beyond mere science. And I cannot but think that it, together with the awe and reverence which have no kinship with base fear, but arise whenever one tries to pierce below the surface of things, whether they be material or spiritual, constitutes all that has any unchangeable reality in religion.'

And again:

' I have never had the least sympathy with the a priori reasons against orthodoxy, and I have by nature and disposition the greatest possible antipathy to all the atheistic and infidel school.'

I wonder how many, if they were asked to guess the author of the paragraphs I have just quoted, would think of Huxley —Huxley the rationalist, the agnostic, the destroyer of orthodoxy's peace and quiet, the bogey-man of thousands of mid-Victorian homes. Yet it was he who wrote those words; and wrote these, too, in 1870, apropos of the new School Boards:

' I have always been strongly in favour of secular education, in the sense of education without theology; but I must confess I have been no less seriously perplexed to know by what practical measures the religious feeling, which is the essential basis of conduct, was to be kept up, in the present utterly chaotic state of opinion on these matters, without the use of the Bible. . . . By the study of what other book could children be so much humanised and made to feel that each figure in that vast historical procession fills, like themselves, but a momentary space in the interval between two eternities, and earns the blessings or the curses of all time according to its effort to do good and hate evil . . . ?' [2]

The truth is, of course, that Huxley was essentially and deeply religious; but that this really obvious fact was

[1] Written on the occasion of the centenary of Huxley's birth.

[2] As the Rt. Hon. J. M. Robertson informs me, Huxley somewhat modified this view in later years. See J. A. Picton, *The Bible in School*, London 1901, p. 12; and Edward Clodd's volume on Huxley, pp. 34–37.

completely masked for the average man of his day by his onslaughts on what that average man imagined an integral part of his religion, but Huxley regarded as a dead-weight, an obstruction to any true religion.

The fact that we to-day can wonder at the popular estimation of Huxley is a measure of the extraordinary change which has come over the whole of this field of thought since his time—a change to which he contributed as much as or more than any other single individual.

When Huxley was a young man, adherence to the Church of England was still a condition of entering College at Oxford and Cambridge. Religion in England meant Anglicanism or else Protestant Nonconformity, and Rome was still to the bulk of the population quite simply the Scarlet Woman. When he was at the height of his activity, between 1860 and 1890, conditions had somewhat changed; but none the less the Established Church was in an entrenched and dominating position which we can hardly picture to-day, the popular knowledge of other religions was negligible, the science of comparative religion had scarcely been heard of, and religion was in general still identified with a somewhat theologically-inclined Protestant Christianity. Any attack on any doctrine of that particular brand of religion was regarded as tantamount to irreligion.

Upon this scene, enter Huxley. He was by temperament a Puritan. He believed passionately not only in the advancement of knowledge, but also in an absolute Truth and an absolute Goodness, in hard work and rigid morality, in beauty of character and of art. The difficulties which he faced and overcame at the beginning of his career, both with regard to his scientific position and to his marriage, steeled and fixed that temperament. When he had made such sacrifices in order to be able to pursue truth, the discovery that most people refused to accept it even when thrust under their noses, only sharpened his pursuit and his zeal in truth's service. His catholic taste, his immense voracity of reading, and his wide circle of friends and acquaintances prevented him from ever becoming narrow-minded through over-specialisation. His professional acquaintance with the value of true scientific method in arriving, even if slowly, at permanent results, made him contemptuous of those who swallowed conclusions on insufficient evidence, and led him to adopt the position for which he coined the title of agnosticism. For instance, he writes:

'The philosopher founded in naturalism . . . is compelled to demand that rational ground for belief without which, to the man of science, assent is merely an immoral pretence.'

Our other chief character is a bomb—the *Origin of Species*, dropped on to the nineteenth-century stage with so much deliberation by that great and quiet man (who had so nearly taken orders in his youth), Charles Darwin.

We all know the result—the bad blood, the ignorant invective, the invective of those who were not ignorant and ought to have known better, the outcry that religion was in danger: and the further result that Huxley felt impelled to enter the fight and to attack all that was untenable in the orthodox religious views of the time, particularly on the theological side. It was thus an accident that he was so much of an iconoclast, so much of a devil or bogey to the orthodox. His Romanes Lecture and many of his essays and letters testify to what constructive force he could have exerted in religious thought if circumstances had been different—a constructive force which would assuredly not have been less than that which he revealed in pure science or in education.

I propose here to give a brief account of Huxley's attitude to religion, illustrated so far as possible by quotations from his writings; and then to try to estimate what he would be doing or saying on the subject if he had lived to-day. I know too well how difficult the latter task will be, and how inevitably personal ideas and prejudices will intrude; none the less, I do not think it an unprofitable occupation.

In the first place, then, Huxley's destructive contribution to religious evolution was important. By concentrating his attack upon dogma and the belief in verbal inspiration, which he stigmatised as Bibliolatry, he helped very materially in freeing the vital core of religion from such superstructures, and in showing how unessential to true religion is most theology. For instance, when he, under the guise of 'the Agnostic,' was attacked by Dr. Wace and told that

'it is, and ought to be, an unpleasant thing for a man to have to say plainly that he does not believe in Jesus Christ.'

he retorted by saying that the ' ought to be ' implied

' A proposition of the most profoundly immoral character';

and continues:

' I verily believe that the great good which has been effected in the world by Christianity has been largely counteracted by the pestilent doctrine on which all the Churches have insisted, that honest disbelief in their more or less astonishing creeds is a moral offence, indeed a sin of the deepest dye.'

This point I need not labour: I would only remind my readers how necessary it was for him, in his day, to labour it.

He was one of the first to perceive the enormous value of a science of comparative religion—a two-edged engine, both destructive weapon and constructive tool. In his well-known essay, *The Evolution of Theology : An Anthropological Study,* he draws a detailed parallel between the religion of the early Hebrews and that of the Friendly Islanders as narrated by Mariner—one of the earliest attempts to do what Sir James Frazer later so thoroughly accomplished. In his opening paragraph he gives us the following passage:

' With theology as a code of dogmas which are to be believed or at any rate repeated, under penalty of present or future punishment, or as a storehouse of anaesthetics for those who find the pains of life too hard to bear, I have nothing to do; and, so far as it may be possible, I shall avoid the expression of any opinion as to the objective truth or falsehood of the systems of theological speculation of which I may find occasion to speak. From my present point of view, theology is regarded as a natural product of the operations of the human mind, under the conditions of its existence, just as any other branch of science, or the arts of architecture or music or painting, are such product.'

Substitue, in the last sentence, ' religion ' for ' theology,' and you obtain as clear a statement as you could want of the standpoint of the modern naturalistic investigator of human biology. What is more, Huxley was in this essay of set purpose confining himself to theology, and undoubtedly would have approved of the application of the sentence to religion as a whole.

We then come to Huxley's position with regard to what many persons (mistakenly, I venture to assert) believe to be the central problem of religion, its necessary keystone—

that of belief in a God. Here the ground had hardly been sufficiently cleared for him to see as we can see to-day, so that his views are of a somewhat negative character. None the less, he has left us some pregnant sayings. Still tinged with the spirit of the age from which he was striving to liberate himself and his contemporaries is, for instance, this passage, implying as it does that God must be a supernatural *person*, in some relation like that of proprietorship to the Universe, a problem not to be approached by scientific methods (and therefore, for Huxley, one on which to be agnostic):

'Of all the senseless babble I have ever had occasion to read, the demonstrations of those philosophers who undertake to tell us all about the nature of God would be the worst, if they were not surpassed by the still greater absurdities of those who try to prove that there is no God.'

Later, in his essay on the School Boards, he wrote, with somewhat similar background:

'I do not express any opinion as to whether theology is a true science. . . . But it is at any rate conceivable that the nature of the Deity and his relations to the Universe, and more especially to mankind, are capable of being ascertained, either inductively or deductively, or by both processes. And if they have been ascertained, then a body of science has been formed which is very properly called theology.

'Further, there can be no doubt that affection for the Being thus defined and described by theological science would be properly termed religion; but it would not be the whole of religion. The affection for the ethical ideal defined by moral science would claim equal, if not superior, rights. For suppose theology established the existence of an evil deity—and some theologies, even Christian ones, have come very near this—is the religious affection to be transferred from the ethical ideal to the omnipotent demon? I trow not. Better a thousand times that the human race should perish under his thunderbolts than that it should say, " Evil, be thou my Good." '

However, in the other essay from which I have already quoted, the *Evolution of Theology*, he closes on a much more modern-sounding note:

'I suppose that, so long as the human mind exists, it will not escape its deep-seated instinct to personify its intellectual conceptions. . . . It may be that the majority of mankind may find the practice of morality made easier by theological symbols.

And unless these are converted from symbols into idols, I do not see that science has anything to say to the practice, except to give an occasional warning of its dangers. But when such symbols are dealt with as real existences, I think the highest duty which is laid upon men of science is to show that these dogmatic idols have no greater value than the fabrication of men's hands, the stocks and the stones, which they have replaced.'

Finally, let me quote one more passage which indicates very clearly the direction which his agnosticism was pursuing:

' If the diseases of society consist in the weakness of its faith in the existence of the God of the theologians, in a future state, and in uncaused volitions, the indication, as the doctors say, is to suppress Theology and Philosophy, whose bickerings about things of which they know nothing have been the prime cause and continual sustenance of that evil scepticism which is the Nemesis of meddling with the unknowable.' (*Science and Morals*, 1886.)

To put it baldly, he was forced by the intransigent attitude of Victorian orthodoxy first of all to think of God in orthodox terms—cruder terms, in all probability, than he would have arrived at if he had been free to excogitate the problem for himself, in quiet and on its merits; and, secondly, to adopt an agnosticism which was not passive, no merely fainéant intellectual gesture, but implied the positive immorality of attempts to draw conclusions from premises which could not be known—the immorality, therefore, of basing a religion on the attributes of the type of God with which his opponents, or certainly the majority of them, confronted him. How he would have reacted to the problem to-day, with the more conciliatory attitude of the Church, with the new discipline of Comparative Religion at his elbow, and with the growth of the positivistic or naturalistic attitude towards the idea of God, is another question.

Meanwhile, we must close with the positive side of the account. Huxley had his beliefs, like every man who has had to find his feet after doubt, perplexity and hard fortune. What were they, and to what extent were they religious in the full sense of the term ? As I have already said, Truth and Morality were his sheet-anchors. Although he was intensely susceptible to beauty, both of nature and of every form of art, he never seems to have understood the need felt by some artists for the erection of aesthetic truth or reality into the central and dominating principle of life. He could feel strongly enough about beauty to write:

'Physical science may and probably will, some day, enable our posterity to set forth the exact physical concomitant and condition of the strange rapture of beauty. But if ever that day arrives, the rapture will remain, just as it is now, outside and beyond the physical world; and, even in the mental world, something superadded to mere sensation.'

But I am unable to recall any passage in his writings where he even mentions the problem of whether for the creative artist the right and wrong of aesthetics are above the right and wrong of morality; and I am tolerably certain that, if he had, he would have indignantly repudiated the doctrine without troubling to discuss it.

Again, although he was perfectly aware of the emotional quality of religion as opposed to the rational (or the practical) quality of morality, and frequently distinguishes the two as ' affection ' and ' science ' respectively, there is no evidence that he was willing to attach any special value to what we are now accustomed to call ' religious experience,' even in its highest and most mystical flights—or at least any value in any way comparable to those which he attached to the intellectual virtues of truth and the practical virtues of morality.

Here, again, it is possible that he would have to-day adopted a different position. For one thing, his opponents were putting all their apples into the opposite basket— of theology and formal faith; for another, Darwinism had not worked itself out to its logical conclusions in philosophy. He had not yet been confronted with William James' pragmatic truth, nor Bergson's keen attack upon intellectual process as itself a product of the evolutionary mill, and therefore itself not merely limited but qualitatively different from other possible kinds of knowledge; nor had biologically-minded anthropologists and philosophers fully and with proper background stressed the survival value, in man's evolutionary history, of the altruistic tendencies, nor attempted to trace in detail the evolution of morality.

I think it would not be unfair to say that he occasionally made abstractions of truth and of morality, that, in other words, he tended to deify them—although he certainly at other times subjected these gods to the most searching analysis. For instance, he could write:

'All truth, in the long run, is only common sense clarified';

or again:

'In whichever way we look at the matter, morality is based on feeling, not on reason; . . . goodness is a kind of beauty. The moral law, like the laws of physical nature, rests in the long run upon instinctive intuitions, and is neither more nor less "innate" and "necessary" than they are. Some people cannot by any means be got to understand the first book of Euclid; but the truths of mathematics are no less necessary and binding on the great mass of mankind.'

Yet at the close of his life, in that famous Romanes Lecture, 'Evolution and Ethics,' which contained his greatest single contribution to moral and religious thought, he nailed his colours to the mast. He started from the problem of evil, and, naturally, dealt with it *sub specie evolutionis*:

'After the manner of successful persons, civilised man would gladly kick down the ladder by which he has climbed. He would be only too pleased to see "the ape and tiger die." But they decline to suit his convenience; and the unwelcome intrusion of these boon companions of his hot youth into the ranged existence of civil life adds pains and griefs, innumerable and immeasurably great, to those which the cosmic process necessarily brings on the mere animal.'

Or again, with regard to various past philosophies and poems, he says:

'The conscience of man revolted against the moral indifference of nature, and the microcosmic atom should have found the illimitable macrocosm guilty. But few, or none, ventured to record that verdict.'

He then proceeds to dismiss the theodicies which are the necessary result of assuming a beneficent divine power immanent in the world and conceived as directing its evolution —theodicies which he finds best epitomised in Pope's lines:

'All nature is but art, unknown to thee;
All chance, direction which we cannot see;
All discord, harmony not understood;
All partial evil, universal good;
And spite of pride, in erring reason's spite
One truth is clear; whatever is is right.'

And this conclusion, from its inception with some of the Stoics to its Panglossic latter end in certain modern evolutionists, he dismisses as fitting for

' an inscription in letters of mud over the style of Epicurus.'

From this he goes on to discuss in good earnest the bearing of evolutionary biology upon the problem:

' The propounders of what are called the " ethics of evolution," when the " evolution of ethics " would usually better express the object of their speculations, adduce a number of new facts and arguments in favour of the origin of the moral sentiments, in the same way as other natural phenomena, by a process of evolution. I have little doubt, for my own part, that they are on the right track; but as the immoral sentiments have no less been evolved, there is, so far, as much natural sanction for the one as the other.'

And finally he comes roundly out with his great exhortation:

' Let us understand, once for all, that the ethical progress of society depends, not on imitating the cosmic process, still less in running away from it, but in combating it.'

Here is indeed a confession of faith. Of faith in the absolute value resident in man's intellectual and moral quests and powers; of faith in the significance of human life, and in particular of its ethical aspect; of faith in a great deal more than his opponents had been willing to credit him with. And yet to some it seemed a confession of the insufficiency of those ideas and methods to which he had most conspicuously pinned his earlier faith, to which he had devoted most of the energy of his prime.

I think that in fact there does in this fine essay reside a certain unresolved contradiction; and I shall try later to show how, perhaps, he might have resolved that contradiction if he were living to-day. For the present, I will content myself with pointing out that his attitude was conditioned in part by the fact that the evolutionary battle was still raging, and that men had not yet had time to see the problem in clearest perspective, nor to work out many of its corollaries and implications; and, secondly, that he was confronted at every turn by theories, principles, and practices which, though to-day half-forgotten or completely mouldering, were then alive enough. There was the doctrine of perfectibility and of inevitable progress which Herbert Spencer had optimistically carried on. There was the ferocious individualism of the *laissez-faire* school, which (even more successfully, though no less vigorously, than other and mutually exclusive principles) was attempting to justify itself by pointing its finger to Mr. Darwin and ' nature red in tooth and claw.' There was the sincere but aggravating school of ' reconcilers ' like Henry Drummond, who wanted to have things both ways at once. And there was Orthodoxy still reclining on her pillow of soporific theology and advocating ideas and practices which Huxley thought both false and childish.

But I am running beyond my limits; and must pass to a brief summing-up of my grandfather's position as it appears (with whatever inevitable imperfection) to one of a later generation who can only judge of him from the printed page.

He fought the joint battle of evolution and freedom of thought to such effect that Darwin, before his death, saw his firebrand theories age into respectability, and achieve not merely toleration but honour and praise; and that England is to-day the country of greatest liberty of speculation, of least acrimony between science and religion. Unorthodoxy is no longer a stigma. We are not so much troubled by politico-religious problems as France or Italy, nor disgraced by the half-baked Fundamentalism of the United States.

The time had come when the religious spirit had to find new forms; to do that the old forms, or much of them, had to be pulled down; and Huxley found himself cast, by the lot of circumstance, for the part of puller-down in chief. So thoroughly, and yet with such lack of vandalism or of any destructiveness for its own sake, did he do his part, that we are already beginning upon constructive work for the new building which will inevitably rise upon the site of the old.

If it had not been for the violent temper of some of the leaders of the Church in the 'sixties, the constructive work might have begun yet earlier. But the Church chose as its attitude the obstinacy of Wilberforce with his ill-mannered taunts, rather than the tolerance and broadminded searching for truth, new and old, of Kingsley.

Huxley, the chief spokesman of science, was not intolerant: he was essentially a religious-minded man. He was on terms of intellectual and personal intimacy with many of the leaders of liberal religious thought both within and without the Churches.

It is of real interest to ask ourselves how he would have responded if the spirit of Kingsley and Jowett had prevailed over that of Wilberforce and Wace. I believe that agreement would have been possible on many matters, and that a state of friendly neutrality, as at present, instead of active hostility, could have obtained between Religion and Science. But could there possibly have been full alliance? Could there have been agreement upon the central issue of present-day theology—the problem of God? When all is said and done, that was, and still is, the real issue. On that issue I do not think that Huxley or any one else of his day could have pronounced. Neither the data nor the requisite background were in existence. Agnosticism on the one side, and either Authoritarianism or the appeal to unanalysed religious experience on the other—those seem to me to have been the only refuges possible to the parties, even if they had wished not to embark on open warfare.

Meanwhile, history ran another course. Looking back on that course, let us rejoice for the sake of the progress of humanity that Huxley was there, ready to undertake his task of beneficent destruction; and let us, in justice to him, realise that his was no partial spirit, but one to whom religion, like all other high human activities, was of vital concern.

An interesting problem that poses itself in this centenary year of Huxley's birth is this—what would be his attitude to the religious life of our time if he were in his prime to-day?

First we must remind ourselves of the changes which have come over the scene between then and now—changes in professing Christianity itself; changes both in the popular and in the specialist knowledge of the diverse forms of religions, with a consequent change in orientation and attitude to the problem; the changes consequent upon the rise of psychology to an autonomous and important science; a change in the relative importance ascribed to creed and worship, theological dogma and religious experience; changes seen in the spread of evolutionary outlook, in the pushing of the evolutionary idea to its logical conclusions, and in the emergence of a fuller body of evolutionary principle.

E

To take this last point first, we must remember that in Huxley's day the doctrine of inevitable progress was still seriously maintained by men of reputation and importance like Spencer. This was, properly enough, repugnant to Huxley's sturdier common sense. He countered it, not by urging a modified or limited doctrine of progress, but by emphasising the undeniable fact that vice equally with virtue, degeneration equally with advance, ruthless selfishness equally with altruism, were all products of evolution, and that stationary persistence of type was to be found as well as constant change.

To-day I do not think even the most ardently orthogenetic biologist would dream of advocating *inevitable* progress. It, like other dreams of the eighteenth-century's humanism, has crumbled when confronted with fact by rigorous critics, most notable among whom in recent years has been Dean Inge. With the decay of this aprioristic and proselytising belief, however, the field lay open for those, more patient, who, instead of asserting what ought to happen, set out to discover what had actually happened. Their analysis has made it abundantly plain that if organic life is considered as a whole there is found, in spite of degeneration and stagnancy, of cruelty and stupidity, an observable direction in its evolution. This direction can be recognised as tending towards the raising of the upper level of achievement attained by life in respect of certain qualities, such as power, efficiency, harmony of parts, and improvement of mental life. Further, since these qualities are on the whole qualities which to man appear good, it is perfectly legitimate to drop the non-committal term *evolutionary direction* and to use in its place that of *biological progress.*

That being so, the antagonism between the cosmic process and human aims is seen to be not nearly so radical as Huxley endeavoured to prove it in his Romanes Lecture. The direction in which both are tending is the same, or at least similar: it is the methods and the pace which are so different. The methods of prehuman evolution are chiefly (though not wholly) those of struggle and elimination, of blind and fortuitous variation sifted by a ruthless natural selection. Those of human evolution come to be more and more those of intelligent guidance and control, the substitution of conscious purpose for unconscious and random variation, of prevention before the event for elimination after, of co-operation for the struggle of each against all. There is, too, a coming into being of values which previously had not existed.

By these means the evolutionary process is accelerated, and raised in large part on to a new plane. It is our duty to keep it on this plane so far as possible, and this we can only do by employing methods very different from those employed by evolving life in previous epochs. But the whole process is a continuous one, and there is no need for any radically Manichean attitude towards non-human ' Nature.'

This leads to another corollary of the evolutionary idea which had not been properly appreciated in Huxley's time. In any movement or process of change, the rate must be considered as well as the direction. A general who wishes to move an army rapidly across country might be forced to abandon certain types of heavy transport because they hindered his mobility: they would go in the direction he wanted, but they would not go fast enough. As a matter of everyday observation, one has only to reflect upon the moral and political likes and dislikes of mankind to perceive that a large proportion of the things which men call bad are so stigmatised because they are moving either faster or slower than men like, and not because they offend against any absolute canon of goodness.

If one's thought has the evolutionary background, one must postulate an optimum rate as well as an optimum direction of evolutionary progress: and if this be admitted, then even things or processes which are moving in the right direction may be evil if they are moving too slowly and so retarding the process as a whole. In fine, the ideas of evolution have made it possible, and indeed necessary, to transfer the simple concepts of relative motion from mechanics to morality.

In this way what is good in one epoch may become harmful in another: and this, too, we must discount unless we are to over-emphasise the antinomy between the microcosm and the macrocosm, between the ideals of man and the slow-grinding processes of the rest of the universe.

Finally, the analysis of thinkers like Bergson and Lloyd Morgan has reminded us that to trace back a thing or a process to simpler origins does not explain it or simplify its essence. The mental processes of an adult man are partly conditioned by those of his childish years, but are in themselves of quite different nature.

Owing to the rise of psychology and of the comparative study of religion, the general attitude of the religious man is far less rigid to-day than fifty years ago. Very few educated people would now maintain that their own religion was wholly and exclusively ' true ' and all others completely ' false.' Religion itself is seen as evolving, and as adapting itself, albeit incompletely, to the changing conditions of civilisation.

The psychological studies of men like Shand and M'Dougall have made it possible for us to assert that the religious ' sentiment ' (in the strict psychological sense) is one which normally, though by no means necessarily, becomes organised in human minds developing in any usual human environment. In the normal adolescent and adult, it is there, waiting an outlet for its expression.

Furthermore, the recent developments of psychology following on the work of W. James and of Freud have shown that a great many phenomena of the religious life which were supposed to require direct divine intervention can be readily accounted for on simpler hypotheses—phenomena such as conversion, sense of grace, visions and inspiration, mystical experience and sense of communion with God, etc. As indicated above, this does not necessarily take away from their intrinsic value: but it makes our attitude towards them other than that of our forbears.

Finally we come to what I see as the crux of the problem. I can see Huxley responding to the increased emphasis laid by the Churches upon the intrinsic value of religious experience. He would say that religious experience is a natural phenomenon like any other, an outcome of the psychic structure of man, and that, if it is thought of in a sensible way, it is to be encouraged in so far as beautiful and satisfying in itself, and in so far as conducive to a richer and better life. I can see him admitting the practical necessity of certain forms of religious symbolism, once the Churches admitted that they were symbolic. I can see him rejoicing in the victory of truth and common sense involved in the gradual abandonment of the belief in the miraculous as a necessary element in religion. I can see him welcoming the view of the more advanced among the leaders of religious thought that religion is no supernatural gift (or infliction !), but a natural phenomenon—one of the highest of natural phenomena, but not supernatural. But I cannot see him coming to terms over the idea of a God who is either personal or superpersonal.

As I pointed out in a previous paragraph, the idea of a personal God, in a position towards the world essentially like that of an absolute ruler to his nation and country, with the added property of creator, permeated the orthodoxy with which Huxley found himself confronted. This idea carried with it such corollaries as the ready possibility of miracle, the validity of purely petitionary prayer, or the idea of propitiatory sacrifice.

This concept, as well as the Absolute of the metaphysicians, Huxley countered with Agnosticism. ' There *may* be such a Being,' he would in effect say, ' but none of the evidence presented satisfies me in the least that there actually *is*. That being so, it is not merely a waste of time for me to discuss the matter until more evidence is adduced, but definitely wrong to base any conclusions, theoretical or practical, upon the assumption of His existence.'

But to-day the liberal wing of religious thought rejects all naïve creationism; rejects miracles; sees in prayer a special form of mediation, of value for the spiritual results which it engenders in the praying mind; sees sacrifice as discipline for the self, not as propitiation of an external power. And the relation of God to the universe is in general conceived either as still personal, but more remote; or, more pantheistically, as immanent and therefore less personal.

I feel fairly confident that Huxley would have continued the ' anthropological ' line of attack so brilliantly begun in his *Evolution of Theology*, for which the work of men like Frazer would have provided him with inexhaustible material. I can see him arguing along some such lines as these: ' The idea of God or Gods is one which is found in the religious beliefs of the majority of men. It is thus a natural phenomenon, to be investigated by science equally with the colour of men's skins or their power to perform mathematical calculations. I will therefore try to investigate it, from as dispassionate and externalised a standpoint as possible, on the evidence which the anthropologists and psychologists have so painstakingly amassed.'

If he had done so, he could not very well have escaped certain conclusions. In the first place, there has been a notable progressive evolution of the idea of God in man's mind. We have only to remind ourselves of the tendency from polytheism to monotheism, and of monotheism to become less and less anthropomorphic. In the second place, it is obvious that the relations (as envisaged by man) of Divinity to the phenomenal universe have become progressively less immediate. Primitive man may suppose a God to inhere in the humblest objects; the idea that striking or unusual natural occurrences, such as thunder, earthquake or pestilence, are the direct result of a Divine operation, is widespread up to a late stage in religious development; so, too, is a belief in the local preferences of particular divinities. Furthermore, the Divinity in the course of time comes to have progressively less to do with the operation of nature. Whereas to primitive man the causation of the simplest phenomena is sought in the capricious and free-will activities of spiritual beings, this conception is gradually replaced by that of natural law. With Galileo and Newton, natural law was seen to extend to all mechanical phenomena, and the physical and chemical worlds were not long in following suit. With Darwin and with nineteenth-century physiology, the same was achieved for the organic world; and twentieth-century psychology is extending the achievement to the world of mind. The stars in their courses demand a God to uphold them neither more nor less than does a falling raindrop to direct its course; the different types of animals require a Creator no otherwise than a lump of clay or a drop of water; nor does the sense of ecstasy or of inspiration demand communion with or direction by a Divine person any more than do common sensation or the simplest operations of arithmetic.

In other words, God or Gods are first conceived of as the active agents in natural phenomena; later, as directing or guiding them; until finally with the extension of the discovery of natural law by science, the place of possible relation between God and phenomena becomes (unless we revert to pantheism) more and more remote, until finally the remoteness tends to become immeasurable.

There are two ways of interpreting these facts. One is to say that the idea of God is an idea framed by man to account, on some unitary basis, for all the varied manifestations with which he is confronted in nature and in his own mind and his relations with other men. Since he himself is a spiritual and personal being, he has almost invariably ascribed spirit and personality to the entity which he postulates as causing or directing phenomena. The idea of God is therefore a convenient symbolism for grasping under a single head the multifarious activities of the universe in their relation to man.

The other possible interpretation is to grant the symbolism, to grant also its frequent imperfection, but to say that it is not only symbolism, but in some degree a representation of a reality, but a reality too large and too complex for us to grasp entire.

As between these two views, I do not think Huxley would have hesitated. He would have accepted the first. The latter he would not have rejected, but would have confronted it with his agnosticism, and by so doing have sterilised it and enfeebled its practical value. For, be it observed, the conception underlying it is essentially that of the static orthodoxy of Huxley's day, only with numerous complications added. The Absolute God exists in some way behind phenomena; and the actual God or Gods worshipped by men are incomplete and symbolic representations of the Absolute God. But no method is suggested, save that of miraculous intervention, by which man's beliefs as to the nature of his actual ' anthropological ' Gods can be brought into relation with, and made real representations of, the postulated Absolute God beyond.

Furthermore, the observed facts can be explained without any such assumption; and Huxley was not one to disregard the principle of the economy of hypothesis.

But even after adopting the first alternative he might have taken up one of two attitudes towards it. On the one hand, he could have continued the intransigent attitude of combatant nineteenth-century science. ' Your idea of God,' he might say, ' is a symbol, a personification of natural forces. Such a method of thinking is an infantile one, to be abandoned as soon as scientific investigation provides an account in accurate terms of the intellect. Besides, your formulation is not only inadequate; it is dangerous. You first personify the powers of the universe; you then assume that your symbol is reality; you then apply deductive reasoning to this assumed reality and regulate your life according to the conclusions logically drawn from those premises. Not only this, but since there exists no verificatory check on your speculations, you personify in your God not only the facts of external nature but your own desires. Your own desires are unfortunately not always good, and so we have the genesis of jealous Gods, revengeful Gods, proud and ultra-patriotic Gods, not to mention the foibles of the polytheistic pantheon."

On the other hand, he might equally well argue thus: ' Granted that a personified God is a symbol, yet our anthropological study has shown that it has always represented, with greater or lesser faithfulness, certain definite realities of nature. If therefore I reject what seems to me the false symbolism of divine personality, a perfectly definite residuum of meaning still attaches to the term God—as definite a meaning as that in the terms " beauty," or " modern European civilisation." It is a term for the powers operating in nature (including in nature, of course, oneself and other men) in so far as they enter into relation with human life, intellectual, emotional, or moral. It is not true to say that we want no such term once the methods of science have provided us with a scientific analysis of phenomena. Such an analysis is always discursive, and always incomplete. We want a unitary term, because it is important to bring ourselves as units into some sort of relation with the universe as a unit, and because the existence of proper terms facilitates thought and action. I therefore retain the term God to denote this very important concept, but deliberately reject the idea of personality in God. The purging of the concept of God of any inherent notion of personality is to me a further step in the evolution of the idea of God, comparable, for instance, to the step from polytheism to monotheism.'

Which of these views he would have adopted it is hard to say. But he would have certainly refused to accept a personal God. He would have denied our ability to extract a knowledge of the personality of the Absolute; but would have been convinced that the personality of the actually-worshipped or anthropological Gods had been entirely supplied by human agency.

But, finally, we can readily see him pushing forward his *Anthropological Study* and making a profound survey of religion as a natural phenomenon—a real Natural History or Biology of Religion. Such a task he could have brilliantly accomplished. Starting from the known inherited mental make-up of man and the fact that men live inside a certain range of environment and tradition, he would have traced the necessary emergence of religion and its gradual evolution. How richly could he have castigated the folly and the emotional and moral bias of early religions, and with what ruthless skill exposed how from false assumptions sprang false conclusions, and how failure to use the critical powers of the intellect led in the long run too often to cruelty, strife, intolerance and hostility to new truth.

But how vividly at the close could he have pointed out for us the direction in which religion is evolving and must evolve, and the conditions which it must obey if it is to play its part in a harmonious civilisation. He would have made clear to us how in any developed religion the emotional, the intellectual, and the practical aspects are all necessary and interdependent. Morality that is solely practical is not religious, nor even if it be intellectually illumined too. He knew well enough that religion is in the first instance an emotional reaction. But he knew equally that this emotional reaction could be, in itself and in its results, either good or bad; and that it could not be wholly or mainly good unless it permeated and was permeated by all other parts of our life, including our intellectual and our practical activities. To be religious in any satisfying way we must, among other things, love truth for its own sake—not for its pragmatic value; and we must do good because we desire the good, not merely because we find it pays to respect the views and conventions of society.

He might well, under the influence of recent psychology, have come to realise more fully the value of ritual as a directly-felt expression of religious sentiment; and of the more ' mystical ' types of religious experience as possessing intrinsic value in the same way as does aesthetic experience or the experience of love. And as a naturalist he would have been the first to admit that different individuals would be expected to excel in and to lay emphasis on different aspects of the religious life.

He himself, in any age or circumstances, would have emphasised the moral and intellectual sides. In a letter of 1892 he writes to Romanes:

' I have a great respect for the Nazarenism of Jesus—very little for later " Christianity." But the only religion that appeals to me is prophetic Judaism. Add to it something from the best Stoics, and something from Spinoza and something from Goethe, and there is a religion for men.'

In any epoch he would have been a most valuable contributor to religious thought, in that he would in any circumstances have helped in clarifying the natural vagueness of the average man's beliefs, and have aided in opposing the normal tendency of strongly-felt religious emotion to claim too much in the spheres of intellect and practice and to set itself up as an absolute standard untempered by tolerance or by the self-criticism of reason.

I do not think that he would have found his views compatible with any form of Christianity as held to-day. Although he would have welcomed the change in outlook which has taken place in the liberal wing of the Church, he would, I am convinced, have seen in it a change which was running parallel with what he conceived to be the right line, but not on the right line itself. Between those two parallel lines a gulf still opens. It is far narrower than it was; but still as profound, and still unbridged.

ON THE HISTORY OF SCIENCE[1]

HISTORY is a mirror in which we may see ourselves, and not only our exteriors, as in a common glass, but, if we choose, our more real selves, stripped of trappings and set on an enduring stage. What we thought novel in our own time is seen as old; although each problem is ever peculiar and demands its individual solution, humanity has long been familiar with it under other disguises; our distresses that we so magnified dwindle when we see the ages' inheritance of pain; our very errors appear as the necessary tentatives of truth, and no longer hang so heavy on our necks; new modes of living are revealed to our inexperience; and in passionless and understanding contemplation of the world's unrolling we may attain to one of the privileges of the Gods.

That is why history, the least valuable of disciplines when unintelligently studied, comes to hold premier place when the fullness of the mind is playing upon it. Such different men as Croce, to whom the natural sciences rank low and art is high, and Wells, who exalts science, and to whom much of art is a closed book, find in history the highest exercise of man, and can do so because they both have active minds whose every faculty, intellectual and intuitional alike, they are content to employ upon its problems.

The history of science is as valuable as constitutional history or the history of politics or the history of religion. The great body of ascertained fact which exists in the records of natural science is of no more value in itself than are machines in themselves or works of art in themselves. There are needed men with knowledge to work the machines, men to whose spirit the works of art may speak. The works of man only live in so far as man vivifies them; and this *corpus* of fact that to some people constitutes the reality of natural science is only a vast stamp-collection, no more than a lumber room, unless each generation in its turn will make

[1] A review of *Studies in the History and Method of Science*, vol. ii. Edited by Dr. C. Singer, Oxford, 1921.

it live. It lives most strongly (so is the human mind constructed) by being woven into the general background of some general philosophy of things. The history of science shows us how a body of fact, comparatively inert and lifeless while held in one framework of opinion, may be seized by another more vigorous movement of the mind and used as a living battering-ram to beat open the doors of progress. This happened, for instance, when the facts of comparative anatomy and embryology were snatched from the hands of the ' nature philosophy ' school and of the teleologists, and used by the evolutionists to effect a great liberation of the human spirit. Paley and Owen were using the same sort of facts as Darwin and Hooker; in the hands of one set of men they evaporated, while the others condensed them to an intenser reality.

The history of science should help us too to discount the fads and fashions of the moment (for it must be confessed that there are fashions scientific as well as sartorial !); it will help us in judging of the practical utility of the methods used by different ages and by different nations; it will help to remind us of the incredible conservatism of the human mind in presence of new facts, and of that curious psychological trait whereby, as it has been said, an opinion is held with a violence inversely proportional to the amount of evidence which can be adduced in its support. It will comfort us by showing the greatest men making egregious mistakes, and falling into the very errors against which we pompously warn our elementary students. In fine, it will give us a perspective not only of the growth of scientific knowledge and theory, but, equally important, of the human mind's relation to scientific problems. At present the teaching of science is for the most part a teaching of fact and of practical method. There are signs, however, that the old humanism of the Universities may be revived in a new way, by making every subject complete in itself, to be dealt with, not only as fact and method, but also as history and as philosophy. If this happy day arrives, courses in the history of science will be as integral a part of scientific training as laboratory instruction.

One of the points stressed by Dr. Singer in his treatment of Greek biology and its relation to the rise of modern biology is the wholly different attitude of the Greek mind to science, a difference crystallised in the difference in the methods of scientific record, and dependent in large part upon a difference in origin.

Modern science is based upon a vast, an almost overwhelming bulk of published records, the majority of which deal with observations of fact or with experiments undertaken in the attempt to verify a hypothesis. The impetus for her advance is derived from the efforts of a large mass of workers, often groping blindly round the roots of their own little problems; direction is given to this struggling mass by the few outstanding men of genius and force; finally, the compelling power of the whole arises from the constant and strict verification of hypothesis, and its as constant application to practice. Through this power, science gradually comes to impose her systems of thought upon other systems. During the last three-quarters of a century she has overthrown traditional theology and stamped her evolutionary concept into the very heart of religious thought; at the present moment, the theory of Einstein and the verificatory experiments springing from that theory are bringing science into a conflict with traditional philosophy. In passing, one might say that the conflict of Galileo's theories and experiments with the traditional philosophy of his time affords an excellent historical parallel with the present situation. The real conflict there, the conflict that mattered in the history of thought, was not with the Church over the motion of the earth, but with the Aristotelians over the speed of falling bodies, with the philosophers over the relative values of authority, speculation, and experiment.

The philosophy of a science comes into being with the advance of science, and overbears traditional philosophy. A corresponding relation is seen between the two in the origins of the modern period of science. Dr. Singer points out that the rise of modern science was, to a degree greater than is usually supposed, independent of the renaissance of classical studies. ' The active extension of knowledge by direct observation . . . began centuries before the learned Greek revival, and received its great impetus long after it. Thus modern science arose largely independent both of philosophy and of scholarship.'

With the Greeks, however, science always stood in a direct relation with philosophy, and a relation which was in most ways a dependent one. And this was because, as Dr. Singer elsewhere points out, ' it was the world in relation to himself and not as a mere objective complex of phenomena that interested and appealed to the Greek.'

Knowledge was equally treasured by ancient and modern. But the ancients had not yet discovered that to preserve the treasure from generation to generation, and to make it available for mankind at large, verification and record were essential—tedious, but essential.[1] To the Greek, the intellectual satisfaction of a well-rounded and personal system of thought was the attraction. That is still an attraction for the great man of science to-day; but he knows that the system of relations between phenomena which we call science is something different from and greater than any systems which men can for the present hope to grasp, and that its growth will in time radically alter any system which they at present hold; and so he is content to labour toward a goal which he cannot perceive.

Comte, in his rough-and-ready classification, indicated that the Greek method was the more primitive; and history is showing that the later method is the more successful.

Other aspects of the same general principle appear in other articles of the book. Mr. Marvin lays stress on the essentially social nature of science; and in so doing dots the i's and crosses the t's of the very readable chapters by Mr. Hopstock on Leonardo da Vinci's anatomical work, and by Mr. Fahie on Galileo. Why was it—it is the first question we ask—that Leonardo, in spite of consummate technical skill, the invention of new methods, the enunciation of new principles and theories, had so little influence upon science, while Galileo had so much? To which the answer is that Galileo was always publishing and discussing his results, while Leonardo locked his up in his notebooks. To this result, doubtless, the different spirit of the two centuries

[1] The same is true of history. Greek history of the classical period is a chronicle of contemporary events. The Greeks had no system of permanent record, such as the Egyptians and still more the Chinese possessed, and their historical perspective must have been very shaky for all events more than a generation or so away from the present.

contributed much, stimulating the one man to unfold himself, sealing up the mind of the other in loneliness; but the fact remains. Leonardo's own saying,

> 'Wisdom is the daughter of Experience,
> Truth is only the daughter of Time,'

is apposite to the issue.

But if science must plod the path of verification, she runs the danger of not using her imagination, not seeing further than the tip of her own nose. This danger is emphasised by Dr. Newell Arber in his chapter on the 'History of Paleobotany.' He speaks of 'the constant error of all the older workers, not one of whom appears ever to have dreamed of how remote the Carboniferous flora is from the British flora of to-day. . . . This mistaken outlook, curiously enough, lingers most persistently even among modern workers.' In other words, our author maintains that, through lack of imagination, the average modern paleobotanist is but a step removed from the diluvial theory which he so laughs at; and, in referring everything to the present for comparison, has scarcely advanced beyond anthropocentrism.

Imagination is needed in science as much as in any other mental activity. But it must not take charge of the scientific mind. If it do, disaster may follow. Witness the paper of the great zoologist, Kölliker, quoted by Dr. Singer, upon the Hectocotylus of the Argonaut. It had been known since 1828 that curious structures covered with suckers were to be found inside the mantle-cavity of the female argonaut. At first it was supposed that these were parasites, belonging to the group of Trematode flatworms. In the 'fifties it was definitely shown that these structures constituted an apparatus for fertilisation, being in reality specially modified arms of the male, which he can fill with spermatozoa and detach at will. But meanwhile Kölliker, having got so near to the truth as to recognise the close similarity of the suckers and skin of the supposed parasite to those of its 'host,' not only proposed the hypothesis that the hectocotylus was a dwarf male similar to those already found in wheel-animalcules and barnacles, but went so far as to describe and figure a complete set of (wholly non-existent !) digestive, respiratory, circulatory, and reproductive organs in the detached arm. And yet we scoff at the monkish author who affirms that he saw goose-barnacles growing upon trees and hatching out into geese!

The history of science is a comforting study, because it makes clear to us that the acquisition of new knowledge and the systematisation of old in the modern world are quite different from what they were in any previous epoch. Those gloomy spirits who are always prophesying the downfall of our civilisation because other civilisations in the past have collapsed, apparently forget this. Their prophecies may be right, but their premises certainly are wrong. Humanity is, biologically speaking, very young. No one expects a boy to tackle the problems of life: and humanity has but just passed out of its boyhood.

BIRDS AND THE TERRITORIAL SYSTEM[1]

MR. HOWARD deserves our gratitude, for he has brought into the limelight a new factor in the life of birds. His conception of ' territory ' and the part it plays in the avian life-cycle was already outlined in his remarkable monograph on the British Warblers. That, however, was costly and not readily accessible; and we are glad that he has devoted a separate work to a consideration of the idea and of its general bearings.

It is refreshing to find field-work leading to conclusions of such wide application. The average ornithologist had begun to think that there was nothing new to be learned from British ornithology at least—nothing but an amplification of our old knowledge. In reality, the most valuable results lie waiting for those who have the interest and the patience. I remember myself with what surprise I discovered that the courtship habits of such a common species as the redshank were scarcely known, and the wonderful pleasure that it was to dig up new facts and new general ideas from the nuptial activities of the crested grebe.

The man who is content to make records or to collect skins and eggs will, unless he spend years of his life in a systematic analysis of his own and others' facts, not get anything from his labours—save the very real pleasure of making the observations. But he who takes the trouble to think out new problems and new lines of attack upon the old will have the same pleasure, and in addition the joy of intellectual discovery. It is the man who is willing to build an observation post in a rookery, to make a detailed psychological study of any common bird, to observe the whole sexual cycle of a species—always with some general idea to guide him—who is likely to achieve results.

As the field studies of Bates introduced us to a new idea —of Mimicry in butterflies—so do these of Howard to a new idea—of Territory. I do not wish to imply that no one

[1] *Territory in Bird Life.* By H. Eliot Howard. (John Murray, 21s.)

had realised or described the existence of territory in birds before Howard; but he is the first who has taken the trouble to work the subject out and to show us its extent and its general significance in relation to other aspects of avian biology. As a result of seasons of patient watching among English fields and woods, he has arrived at the conclusion that practically all our birds, when the mating season comes round, stake out a territory for themselves, and that this territory is in most instances the pivot on which their sexual life turns. Usually it is the male who annexes the territory, spending all or most of his time in a given, limited area which he defends from other males; and this annexation occurs long before he appears to manifest any interest whatever in the females. We find that this occupation of territory takes place in essentially the same way in migratory and non-migratory forms, and in forms belonging to the most widely different groups. In the warblers, the males come over from their winter-quarters a week or more before the females. They then occupy a definite area, fighting if need be, for its possession, and spend almost the whole of their time in singing—and the song is usually more brilliant before than after the arrival of the females! Song is thus primarily an advertisement, only secondarily a mode of courtship. When the females arrive, there is no courtship in the ordinary sense; on the contrary, the males seem to be almost oblivious of their future mates, and any fighting there may be is between females, for the possession of the occupied territory! Only after the territory is thus staked out, and occupied by a pair of birds, do the activities begin which are usually summed up as 'courtship'—a very poor term in this case; the male assuming the most extravagant attitudes and performing actions obviously directed at the female.

In non-migratory passerine birds like the finches and buntings, the same sort of procedure is gone through. Yellow-hammers, for instance, during the winter collect in flocks on the stubbles. As spring begins, male birds will detach themselves from the flock for a short period each day, and repair to a particular stretch of hedgerow, in which they will spend most of their time on a particular tree, singing. As the season advances, they will spend less and less time with the flock, more and more in the territory, in ever greater activity of singing—until at length the flock has disappeared, since the females finally leave it too, and search for a mate and a home, as in the warblers.

Even in quite a different order of birds the behaviour is similar. Peewits have their territories round the nest, staked out in just the same way by the males in early spring, some time before any sexual activity proper is in evidence at all.

In fact, Mr. Howard claims that territory in some form or other plays a part in the life of all birds, and substantiates his claim for the most unlikely forms—promiscuously-mating species like the cuckoo, gregarious cliff-dwellers like the guillemot, and even (though here, it must be confessed, with considerable limitations) polygamists like the blackcock or ruff. Not only does he make this claim, but I think it must be allowed that he substantiates it.

Territory is most important of all in forms, like the warblers, where the young are hatched naked, and cannot be left long uncovered without risk of dangerous chilling. Here the size of the territory is regulated according to the food-supply and the ability of the parents to find it, and the pair spend the whole of the breeding-season within its confines. A similar state of affairs holds for kingfishers, which divide up their rivers into sections. The crested grebes, on the other hand, make the open water a common fishing-ground, and only delimit territories round their nests in the fringing beds of reeds. Finally, in such birds as the guillemots and other cliff-dwellers, whose nesting space is exceedingly limited, but whose feeding-ground is the unbounded sea, the territory is restricted to a few square feet upon a ledge of rock. It is none the less real for that, and the same instincts are displayed to stake out claims, the same fights occur for possession.

However, it is clear that the nesting-territory of birds like the guillemot is of a different order of importance from the nesting-plus-feeding territory (which we may call *feeding territory* for short) of birds like the warblers.

During the breeding-season, the whole instinctive life of the bird is conditioned by the territory first and foremost, and only in lesser degree by the presence of its actual or potential mate. Of this curious fact, which holds most rigorously in the common monogamous birds, Mr. Howard

gives a number of instances. For example, he observed
how the male lapwings which had detached themselves
temporarily from the flock, and were occupying territory,
were quarrelsome and impatient of intruders, whether male
or female, while the same birds during a part of the day
when they had returned to the flock were as good-natured
as the rest. But if the flock happened to be frightened up
into the region of the territories, their occupiers would be
just as jealous of the presence of the flock as of single birds.
Further, in this stage of the yearly cycle the males took no
particular interest in the females.

It is impossible to go into more detail here. The theory
of Mr. Howard in most general terms may be stated as follows.
Territory in some form or other is of prime biological importance in the life of birds (and probably of other groups
as well). The first sign of sexual activity—the first effect,
presumably, of the vernal change in the sexual organs—
is in most species seen in the instinct of the males, not, as
has usually been assumed to seek out the females, but to
find, occupy, and defend a territory. So far as there is choice
of mates in monogamous species, it is by the females, who
seek out the males; but they only compete for those males
who are in possession of territory. Even when the pair is
established in the area, the occasions when the female is the
primary object of the male's actions is only during
the so-called courtship, whose function is to stimulate the
female psychically and bring her to the condition in which
pairing may be accomplished; but both male and female,
singly and as a pair, still react to the fact of territory, and
are always active in its defence. Mr. Howard quotes an
illuminating observation: he saw a weasel passing through
the territory of a pair of reed-buntings, who were pursuing
it in rage. Another male of the same species of bird
approached. But instead of welcoming it as an aid in driving
off the intruder, the male whose nest was actually in danger,
several times left the pursuit of the weasel to attack the other
reed-bunting!

It is clear that such a concept is of great importance,
both as something new in itself, and as exerting a marked
influence upon our theories of sexual selection. The primary
sexual instinct of insectivorous birds becomes the instinct

to occupy territory; the primary function of their song is to advertise the possession of territory.

One general point which Howard hardly mentions is this—that birds with feeding-territories are the first organisms to practise a regulation of numbers. Birds which cannot secure a territory cannot breed. They appear often to collect into flocks and wander about, frequently at the northern limit of their range. Carr-Saunders has shown us that a regulation of population is practised by all primitive peoples. This, of course, adjusts population to available food supply, and ensures moderate numbers with good development instead of great numbers with stunted development. Birds, though unconsciously, accomplish the same result.

Here and there Mr. Howard has perhaps generalised a little too far. The mental life of birds is more varied than most people think, and their life-histories show most remarkable divergencies. Mr. Howard has for the most part confined himself to the song-birds and the waders. In other groups, things sometimes are a little different. For instance, in the crested grebe, hostility between pairs does not seem to be manifested only within the boundaries of the territory of one of the pairs, but anywhere. This would mean that the mate plays a more important part in conditioning the mental reactions than in warblers or buntings. Again, in herons and egrets (at least in the two American species with whose habits I am familiar), it is not the male who seeks out the territory long before pairing-up, but pairing-up occurs on the communal feeding-grounds, and the couple then, deserting the flock, *together* choose and occupy a nesting-site (often abandoning one or two sites before finally satisfying themselves). Mr. Howard also believes that one bird of a pair which is in possession of territory will never desert its mate in favour of another bird. However, the female of a pair of black swans which recently came under observation not only deserted its mate for an older bird, but now takes an active part in driving off her former husband, whenever he appears upon the scene.

These, however, are minor points. The main thesis stands, and will remain of prime importance for our understanding of the life of birds. The general biologist no less than the naturalist and the lover of birds should read and ponder this book.

AN HOUR'S PSYCHOLOGY

MIND you go and hear Janet; and tell me all about it when you get back.' I was going up to London, and that was my message from a psychological colleague. Professor Janet was lecturing at the Royal Society of Medicine. I went, I heard, and was conquered. The lecture was a work of art and stuffed as full of meat as an egg. I made notes at the time for my friend. Now, in an interval of leisure, I glance at them, and decide that it would be worth while to put them into shape.

After a lightning sketch of brute minds—starting as pure mechanical reflexes, leading up through perceptive processes to those in which all faculties collaborate to execute a single action—we came to the gulf between brute and man. Professor Janet does not think that gulf so broad as it is often painted. He bridged it with one span—of language. ' L'homme, c'est l'animal bavard. Il bavarde avec les autres; et quand il se trouve seul, il bavarde avec lui-même. La pensée, c'est un éternel bavardage intérieur.'

But what *is* language? Language is a mode of action. It is in its origin (here was a new window on to things!) a combination of an action of the mouth with (let us say) an action of the legs, as when an animal utters a definite sound whenever it starts to walk. All action is by language made double, executed similtaneously by the tongue and by limbs or jaws or body. ' Le mot " marcher," c'est une manière de marcher.' (How much happiness is thrown away by men who have not learned that to say ' I love you ' is a mode of loving! To love alone is not enough; one must say so, too!)

But what next? Movements of the tongue are much more economical than those of the rest of the body; so comes the tendency to liberate language from its association with action—the genesis of free ideas. This is the pre-logical stage of mind, the stage in which most savages live. Gradually, much of language becomes so far divorced from reality that it becomes meaningless. ' Si on répète, *marchons, marchons,* et on ne marche pas, comme à l'opéra, alors le mot " marcher" cesse d'être une manière de marcher.' The word must be connected up again with the realism of action; and so, at certain levels of man's genesis, we find promises, pledges, honour, playing an apparently exaggerated rôle in his life. ' Ce sont, en effet, des liaisons entre des mots et des actions.' From this stage springs another, in which belief becomes the dominant factor of the mind and action. Belief is a promise of action. ' I believe that the weather will stay fine '—' ça veut dire, je promets de ne pas porter un parapluie quand je sors '—and this, though on a grander scale, applies to moral and religious beliefs as well. From beliefs springs the notion of *beings*, of Existence as the be-all and end-all of thought.

Is this the end? No: Innumerable defects remain. We are prone to think, or at least to say, that our will, our beliefs, are generally based on reason. ' Hélas ' (there was a world in that *Hélas !*) . . . ' C'est trop amusant de faire des promesses, de croire: et alors . . .'

We have not yet gained reflection; and so are at the mercy of the momentary importance of a word, an idea, an impulse. We commit violences, only to be sorry for them, because they have been the product solely of a part of us. Reflection is the beginning of the logical life. By it all the faculties are summoned to a parliament before the man acts. And because each has had its chance of being heard, so now action pledges them all as a vote pledges an assembly, and only now is reached a truly *personal* stage of being. With this comes the substitution of Reality for Existence as our fundamental notion; and there are many mental patients who lose the sense of reality without losing that of being.

But even so our man is far from perfected. He has personality; but he is a great egoist. ' Ne le blâmez pas: C'est déjà très beau d'être égoïste. Ily a des imbéciles qui ne peuvent pas être égoïstes.' Passionate for what he likes, he will try to avoid doing anything which he does not like; and so, to avoid it, he becomes a liar. ' Personnel, égoïste, passionné, paresseux, menteur—enfin, c'est un caractère comme un autre . . .'

What are the final stages? Morality is the next. M. Janet, shrugging his shoulders, excused himself for being so un-

inspiring: ' La morale, c'est faire les choses ennuyeuses.'
But how is this possible? It becomes possible by means of
a new psychological mechanism; by a mental police force.
If a Martian were to visit London, he would readily understand the functions of those who were making bread, or
boots, or even books. But what, he would say, is the use of
all these men standing about in blue and doing nothing?
The answer is that, in the long run, they are there to see that
the laws are obeyed, and that the boot-makers and bread-
makers continue to make boots and bread even if they do
not want to. The moral stage of mind is characterised by
policeman-tendencies, or, if you prefer, *ergatic* tendencies.
Imposed in the first instance from above, by owners of slave
labour, they have been made personal and in some degree
voluntary by the intermediation of the great religions,
which have harnessed man's laziness to his secret fire for
doing good, and to what Mr. Trotter calls the herd-instinct;
so it comes about that ' morale et travail, c'est la même
chose'; and ' travail et corvée, c'est la même chose.' One
step further is to insert rational consent to morality and to
work, in place of irrational consent or mere compulsion—
Life begins to be reasoned.

Life *begins* to be reasoned . . . what a gulf between this
and the old conception of reason as the basic property
of humanity! Expansion on this level leads to what? To
systems of thought; to the Philosopher. That is its great
default; for the systems are always too small for reality,
and the Philosopher, acting Procrustes, cramps life. ' Les
philosophes sont bien des êtres supérieurs aux animaux
et aux sauvages, mais enfin, il y a mieux.' Two lessons remain
to be learned. One is Science—in other words, the power
of profiting by experience. ' One of the most marked characteristics of savage races is their impermeability to experience'; and this, too, characterises many mental diseases.

Philosophers often confuse memory with habit. But
habit involves action; memory may be a neutral thing,
dissociated from any action. The scientific habit of mind,
' c'est l'habitude d'obéir aux idées sans force psychologique
immédiate.' We are all experimentalists in our degree;
but only by this habit of mind do we become preponderatingly so; only by this do we discover Truth.

There are those to whom Truth is the final Goddess. Their morality is engaged in the service of Truth. But there can be a bondage to truth, and until we are *free* there is no perfection. The escape of thought from the imperfections of the actual into a thought-organised ideal is Art; its projection, dragging present action with it into a more perfect future, is true Religion. Professor Janet prefers to sum up these final modes of mental action, this last lesson of developing mind, as the artistic tendencies. It is they that issue in freedom and in beauty. Only when we combine our search for verifiable truth with these utmost aspirations do we become perfect men. That is why the ' mere ' scientist is not great; that is why art or literature without the passion for truth is trivial and empty. The true man would be he who was always combining, in every activity, this whole hierarchy of mutually reinforcing modes of mind.

To compress his matter within the hour, Professor Janet adopted the linear outline I have sketched. That must, and no doubt will, be modified; for the series is, of course, not so rigid. None the less, it is probably the usual series. If we look back upon our own mental evolution, or reflect upon the probable evolution of the species, we perceive it. As more novel, but equally valid, evidence, we find that patients suffering from various mental complaints reverse their line of progress and descend by these steps to lower and lower stages.

Zoologists are always telling us that the whole of the human race constitutes a single species. That is true if we allow infertility on crossing to be a test for separateness of species. But when we come to diversity of racial constitution of mind, and still more to diversity of individual mental structure, we find that the variety of shapes assumed by mind in the human species—mental organisms if you will—is as multifarious as the variety of physical shapes assumed by lower forms of life. Progress, divergence, specialisation, adaptation, degeneration, play the same part as in physical evolution.

The practical bearings of this are twofold. The first is that, since the mind is the dominant organ of man, different classes of society and different individuals within these classes will inevitably belong to ' mental species ' which will not only be at different evolutionary levels, but may lie along divergent evolutionary lines. To this has come the equality of mankind !

Secondly, such an outlook necessitates its own philosophy of life. Professor Janet was categorical in his stressing of the idea that all these different tendencies and modes of life were necessary to a true and full existence—indeed, to a truly healthy existence—but that they must stand in a definite relation to one another, the higher being founded on the lower, the lower definitely subordinate to the higher. If we think thus, we cannot be ascetics or puritans; we cannot be mystics or pure idealists; we cannot be simple materialists, or pure philosophers, or only men of the world or aesthetes. To be any of these is to divorce one mode of mind from the rest. We should never be content until we have all modes at our command, and all in harmony. . . .

But six o'clock struck; and out of the immense world projected by thought we stepped into Wimpole Street.

EVOLUTION AND PURPOSE

THE argument from design has had a curious history. It was Paley who started Darwin on his intellectual career, as the great evolutionist himself tells us. Later, the identical facts which had served the theologian were made to serve the biologist—only the conclusions were differently drawn. Under the rubric of adaptation, all the phenomena which so much impressed Paley and the Bridgwater school appeared as the raw material of biological orthodoxy in the text-books of evolution. Meanwhile, however, the physiologists had been going a step further in their positivistic materialism; to them, any idea of purpose was still tarred with the theological or at least the metaphysical brush, and they confined themselves for the most part to what events have shown to be a narrow and partial view-point. It is only in the last twenty years that, as for example the classic work of Sir Charles Sherrington shows, they have come ungrudgingly into the evolutionary fold and dealt without qualms in adaptational ideas. With this, the transformation of the original conception was, it would seem, complete. The old, full-blooded teleology of Paley—this 'carpenter theology,' as its opponents nicknamed it—postulating an anthropomorphic artificer for every 'evidence of design' and each single adaptation, has given place in the realm of science to the modern idea of *pseudo-teleology*, in which 'evidence of design' turns out to be in reality evidence of natural selection, and we no longer speak of the purpose, but of the function, of any adaptation or mechanism useful to its possessor.

Meanwhile, the theological doctrine of teleology, though put out of court entirely in its crude form in the post-Darwinian struggles, has also been modifying itself, keeping itself alive in the flux of existence by continual adaptation.

I have been reading a pamphlet by Canon Storr[1] which prompts these reflections. It shows, in the first place, what enormous change has been wrought in orthodox thought

[1] *The Argument from Design.* Rev. V. F. Storr, M.A. (Longmans, Green, 1920.)

by the once-hated and reviled doctrines of evolution. As
our author perhaps somewhat mildly puts it, ' theologians
. . . were at first inclined to oppose evolutionary science.'
When we remember the charges of atheism, immorality,
intellectual perversity, and general wickedness which were
hurled at Darwin and his followers, this might be regarded
as an understatement. However that may be, the advantages
finally reaped by theology from the intellectual labours of
biology are very great. She is no longer confined in a
strait-waistcoat of static dogma, but is learning to
conform her thought to reality, and not to her own wishes or
imaginations.

The Canon starts from the proviso that Paley's position
' has unquestionably been shattered by evolutionary science.'
The new teleology which he sees arising on the ruins of the
old draws its inspiration from the idea of evolution. It may
be briefly summarised thus. In the first place, we must envisage
the *whole* evolutionary process; there has been progress
in the rise of organisms, culminating in man with his conscious personality; and this progress is to be explained by
the idea of purpose behind it. Then, we must never forget
that ' the end explains the beginning, and not the beginning
the end '; man's personality, therefore, has more explanatory
value than any other biological fact. Thirdly, man ' naturally
and inevitably tends to read the world outside him in terms
of himself.' And finally, the teleologist's ' main contention
is that the adjustments and adaptations of the natural order
must be referred back to an intelligence.'

The outcome of the whole train of thought is a rather
Wellsian conception of God, in some way immanent in
the evolving world—and yet transcendent.

It is all very suggestive, very interesting, often very close
to truth, and yet it will not hold water as a complete whole.
When we examine it closely, we find that the reason for its
failure, as for the failure of so many attempts to reconcile
natural science and revealed religion, is that it is trying to
piece together two modes of thought which cannot be recon-
ciled. In the scientific habit of thought we build upon ascer-
tainable fact, whether in physics, or in biology, or, as in
James' *Varieties of Religious Experience*, in religion. But
the other, the dogmatic habit of thought, makes assertions

which go beyond verification—and then proceeds to draw consequences from them.

The best example of this in Canon Storr's pamphlet is his treatment of biological progress. What are the facts? Briefly, they are that in size, in power, in complexity, in independence of the environment, in capacity for knowledge, and in intensity of feeling—in all these and in other ways there has been a progressive increase in the capacities of living organisms during our planet's history. It has happened not only along one, but along many evolutionary lines. Furthermore, judged by our own standards of value, the later stages are higher than the earlier. The teleologist then goes on to assert that this progress is a proof of purpose on the whole scheme, while ' from the point of view of mechanism . . . the whole is simply an unending process of re-distribution of material particles.' On the contrary, he is wrong in both assertions. When we men act so that a desirable result is produced, it is usually the outcome of a mental process which we call purposive activity. But to argue that all processes which are similar *in result* must therefore be accompanied by purposeful activity is really so puerile a piece of logic that one can only be amazed that the contention is still so widely made. As a matter of fact, it was precisely this which Darwin once and for all disproved.

But to assert that to mechanism the process must be meaningless is equally unjustifiable. We cannot say that it is *purposeful* until we are privileged to know what processes occur in the thought of God; but we can and must on the evidence say that it has *direction*. On the average, the upper level of biological attainment has been continuously raised. Not only this, but our own standards, moral, aesthetic, and intellectual alike, have been produced by the process and tend to continue the direction of evolution in the future along the line it followed in the past—towards ' more life.' That being so, we must say that those actions which tend to help the advance of the upper level of living matter—to-day represented by man—along a continuation of the line it has followed in the past, are *good;* while those which tend to hinder it are *bad.* Through evolution, moral values become entwined with verifiable facts outside the sphere of human life. Not merely does mechanism not see evolution as a mere

sequence of non-significant events, but the latest triumph
of mechanistic thought—the Darwinian theory of evolution
—has at last given man that assurance for which through
all his recorded days he has been searching. It has given
him the assurance that there exists outside of himself a
' power that makes for righteousness '; that he is striving
in the same direction as the blind evolutionary forces which
were moulding his planet æons before his appearance;
that his task is not to oppose, but to crown the natural order;
to transform it to a better, not by taking a new direction,
but by accelerating and intensifying the old. All our evidence
points to the fact of conscious purpose having arisen during
the course of evolution, as a better implement for more
rapid progress in the ascent.

A somewhat similar confusion exists between two ideas
of God. There is the idea of God as an absolute conception;
and there is the idea of God to be derived from reasoning
on the facts of nature and the facts of religious experience.
The first is alien to the scientific habit of thought; we are
asked to build up God from our notions of what God ought
to be—and then proceed to deduce consequences from this
unverifiable idea. If there is a God, He must be all-powerful;
if He is all-powerful, He could have prevented the war . . .
and so on to an infinity of useless speculation. The other—
but that would need a chapter. The great theologian of the
future will be he who, boldly asserting that we can never
know the nature of God as absolute, will put on a firm logical
and pragmatic basis that highest synthetic concept of the
human mind for which alone the word God should be reserved.
That concept must be self-consistent throughout; it must
take into account the facts of nature—cosmological and
evolutionary; it must reckon with the desires and hopes,
the struggles and weaknesses of the human mind, and with
its capacity for mystical experience; it must never for one
instant go beyond fact, but it must deal with the highest type
of mental experience equally with the familiar and the physical.
Such a concept, such a God will sustain the civilisations of
the future.

But even the most advanced of the orthodox waver between
the two concepts. In Canon Storr's case, for instance,
the influence of the first concept appears in passages such

as this—' unless my ideals of Beauty and Goodness are mere day-dreams, I must postulate a true ground for them in ultimate reality '—instead of being content with the proximate but no less real reality of his own and other people's experiences and ideals of Beauty and Goodness. But elsewhere the other concept plays its part. ' A God who dwells in calm and splendid isolation is not a God who can meet the urgent needs of a struggling humanity '—and so presumably cannot exist.

Theology is in a period of transition. It knows the reality and value of religious experience, but still approaches the task of interpretation from the old, unjustifiable standpoint of revelation, of dogma, of unverified speculation. Signs are not wanting that it is learning to use the humbler but more lasting method of using fact as the touchstone. But the two methods cannot be combined. It must reform its currency. Samuel Butler gave the State of Erewhon two currencies: there was the ordinary one used for buying and selling goods; and there was the Musical Bank money, of use only in the places of worship. When religion shall agree with the rest of the intellectual world upon a common currency of thought, and refrain from issuing Musical Bank paper in such large quantities, then, and only then, shall we be able to dream of a religion of civilisation, a religion that makes for unity instead of discord, for progress instead of standing still.

THE FROG AND BIOLOGY

THE frog is a too often despised animal,

> 'Whom there are few to praise,
> And very few to love.'

It is small, defenceless, clammy, and rather ludicrous. But it is an organism, and one belonging to the same group of animals as man: it has, for the biologist, the merit of being abundant and easily procured, and that not only as adult but in all stages of its life-history. So it comes about that we know more about the frog, or rather about a number of processes in its life, than about the corresponding processes in any other single organism. 'Know me, know my frog' —that is, I think, a legitimate adaptation of the old proverb for the biologist.

Do not imagine that I can even touch upon one-tenth of the biological problems packed into this little body. I only hope to show a few of the ways in which Frog may be profitably employed as text for biological sermons.

You remember Herrick's lines on a praying child:

> 'Here a little child I stand,
> Heaving up my either hand,
> Cold as paddocks though they be,
> Here I lift them, Lord, to thee.'

A paddock or puddock is a frog, as I expect you all know; and frogs are certainly cold. Many people lump together the coldness of snakes and lizards with that of frogs; but in reality the two are quite different. The snake has a smooth dry skin; the frog a clammy wet one. This clamminess has a meaning. The frog breathes in part through its skin, while snakes, like dogs and men, do not. For such cutaneous respiration the skin must be kept moist, for gases will not pass through a dry membrane, but the oxygen must actually enter into solution before it can be passed into the blood, and carbon dioxide stay in solution until it is in contact with the air if it is to be expelled from the body.

It might be supposed that it was a convenience to supplement one's lungs with one's skin as a breathing organ: and so no doubt in some ways it is—but on one condition. That condition is that the animal live in moist surroundings, for otherwise its skin, which must be wet and thin to exercise its respiratory function, would dry up.

Our frog, that is to say, is a land animal, if you like; but an animal of moist land only. It is a compromise between the aquatic and the terrestrial, emancipated only in part from the watery home of its ancestors.

The more we study the frog the more examples of such compromise do we find, notably in its skeleton, the architecture of its skull, the structure of its heart, and its life-history, in life-history perhaps most strikingly of all.

When I was a small boy, we used often to go and stay in the country with an aunt. Sunk in one corner of the garden was a large tank, perhaps six or eight feet deep, with vertical walls of cement, and more or less full of rain-water and duckweed. In the spring, this used to be occupied by quantities of frogs and toads. These set up a fine chorus of croaking (though why the soft pretty cooing of the toad should be called a croak I do not know), and we often came down to look at them as they lay suspended in the water, eyes and nose just emerging, forelegs spread, and body and hind-legs trailing diagonally down.

Somehow or other we discovered the fact that they liked to scramble on to any floating piece of wood in the water; and we used to spend hours giving the frogs a ride. We took a straight log from the wood-pile, and, quite illegally, hurled it in the water. The frogs (I can see them now) swam from all sides and climbed out upon it. Then with long hazel sticks we propelled the log from one end of the tank to the other. It would rotate a little, and spill the less skilful of its passengers; and it was our amusement to see them try to mount again in mid-course. Some of them, however, were very expert, and would stick on for long journeys.

I do not know why this pleased us so much, but it did; and it remains as one of the vivid memories of the place. However, to discuss that would take us into the biology of other organisms than frogs!

F

The frogs came to the tank in the spring to breed. But what we boys did not think of was the fact that although they could easily enough get in, they could not get out: and that therefore none of their offspring would ever be able to come out on land, but would perish with their parents in the water at the base of those unscaleable walls.

Why did the frogs come to breed in the tank? They came because it was the nearest piece of water, and because frogs must breed in water. Their eggs are fertilised outside

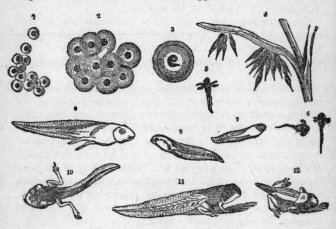

FIG. 8.—Development of the Frog.
1, 2. Eggs. 3. Unhatched embryo. 4–5. Just hatched tadpoles. 6. External gills still prominent. 7–8. Gills grown over by gill-cover. 9. Beginning of hind-leg development. 10, 11, 12. Metamorphosis.

the body, and will dry up if not in water; and they develop into tadpoles, which can only breathe and feed and move in water. Not merely this, but in many essentials of structure the tadpole *is* a fish—in the arrangement of its gills and the blood-vessels that supply them, in its heart, the fin along its tail, and the special sense-organs for perceiving low-frequency vibrations in water which, like a herring or any other fish, it carries on a 'lateral line' along its flank.

There can be no doubt whatever from all the different lines of evidence which we have at command that frogs are actually descended from fish, even if from none of the common types of fish with which we are familiar; and that is to say that they once spent the whole of their life in the water. Now the difficulties attendant upon emancipation from water into air press much harder upon the early than upon the late stages of development. The act of fertilisation itself must be accomplished in a fluid medium. The delicate tissues of the egg and embryo must be bathed in fluid. Life in a fluid with weight supported by displacement is far simpler for the early stages of the animal when the skeleton has not yet been formed.

These difficulties can be and have been surmounted by all the highest land vertebrates. Fertilisation becomes internal instead of external. The great biological invention, the amnion, came into existence—an overarching membrane grown by the embryo for its own protection, enclosing it in a resistant water-cushion, or, as one writer picturesquely puts it, enabling the embryo to live and develop within its own private pond. The private pond in its turn is protected in a hard shell, tight packed with weeks' or even months' supply of provisions; or else is still more efficiently sheltered and victualled within the body of the mother. Only so do vertebrates become truly terrestrial, for only so do they become independent of water at all stages of their life-history.

This emancipation from the water was one of the few large steps in the progress of vertebrates from some primitive lamprey-like form. First the early acquisition of limbs, jaws, teeth, and bone; then this conquest of the land: then the stabilising of the animal's temperature; and finally the development of mind to its highest pitch. In a sense, the transition to terrestrial existence was the most abrupt of all, save the transition from irrational to reasoned life: so it is natural that the adjustment should need time, and that many makeshifts should come into being.

When the biologist shows his pupils that the frontal or the parasphenoid bones of the frog's skull can be easily detached from the underlying parts, he is really demonstrating that the frog has reached a compromise between the early bony fish, with their true skull quite isolated inside the heavy armour of bone in their scaly skin, and the beautifully unified organ exemplified in the skull of a bird or mammal.

The frog's heart is a tissue of compromises between an organ designed to supply the fish's gills and one fully adapted to breathing by lungs. The three pairs of arterial arches; the undivided ventricle with its mixture of arterial and venous blood; the partial separation effected by the valves—all these are marks of a transition. The relatively large amount of cartilage retained in the frog's skeleton again was destined in higher forms to be swept away in favour of the more terrestrially efficient bone. The soft and moist skin is a compromise: for 'nothing like leather' eventually became the motto of terrestrial life. The whole-hearted game of young frogs to play at being fishes is given up in favour of the shadowy and, one might almost say, merely symbolic reminiscences run through by the embryos of true land forms within the egg or womb.

Very well, you may say: but if evolution has brought the frog-type into being, why did it not bring it to a still higher level of existence? If progressive change is one of the laws of evolution, why is it that there are species and groups which do not progress, but stand still, resting on their evolutionary laurels? The question is a fundamental one, and one which has exercised many minds. But the answer, I believe, is not so difficult as at first sight appears.

The organic world develops in a constant condition of what we may symbolise as pressure—the pressure of the inorganic environment, the pressure of enemies, of competition for food and space and mates.

Anything which will give an organism an advantage in the struggle against environment or enemies or competitors of its own blood will reduce this biological pressure. This is especially true where a real progressive variation is concerned, where some character is developed which enables a species to invade hitherto untrodden fields—in other words to invade a low-pressure area; or when the pressure is reduced through the development of some improvement of general organisation—a procedure comparable to the reorganisation of a business from within.

Let us now take a concrete case. Why, when the amphibian type gave rise to the reptilian, did not all amphibia become transformed, or why did those which failed to do so not become extinct under the stress of the new competition from the improved type? The answer is that the great advantage gained by the reptiles lay in the opening up of a whole new area to vertebrate colonisation. In the old area already colonised, their advantage, if any, would not be so great; and in parts of it (for instance the swampier regions) the old type filled the bill so perfectly that the advantage lay on their side. Precisely the same considerations hold good for the inventions of man. The wheeled horse-drawn vehicle ousted the riding and pack animal as the chief means of transport, to be ousted in its turn by the mechanically-propelled vehicle. But there are still particular places, and particular kinds of transport, in which the horse-drawn vehicle still has advantages over the motor, and still other regions in which any wheeled vehicle is at a disadvantage. As a result the old types do survive, though restricted, alongside the new. So the largest and the most progressive types of amphibia perished in competition with the reptiles; but there is a niche well filled by the amphibian type, and competition is not enough to oust the inconspicuous and specialised forms that remain in it.

The distribution of frogs over the earth's surface illuminates what we have been saying. Why is it that frogs and toads are much more abundant, especially in number of species, why do they grow to larger size, towards the equator than towards the poles?

Pole-wards, they actually die out before reaching the Arctic zones. For this there is a physical reason, in their cold-bloodedness and their restriction to fresh water. They would be frozen solid in the winter; even in the summer, if they survived the freezing, they would be so slowly-working that their growth would be prolonged over an uneconomic number of seasons. But the further we advance towards the tropics, the less disadvantageous will their cold-bloodedness be compared with the constant high temperature of birds and mammals, and the more will the difference between the rates of living of the different groups tend to disappear. In the tropics, therefore, it will be more difficult to oust the cold-blooded animal from his niche, and as a matter of fact we do find a general zonal arrangement in the distribution of the land vertebrates, the amphibia and reptiles being relatively important in the warm zones, the mammals the most important in the temperate regions, and the birds (with their power of flight from winter cold) in the Arctic.

Even the fact that the northern and central United States possesses many more and some much larger frogs and toads than northern and central Europe presumably depends upon these same facts, for the mean summer temperature is considerably higher in the United States than with us.

But we are falling into the vaguenesses of generalisation. Let us return to the particular. The frog compromises with its aquatic past by existing in the form of a tadpole through the early part of its life. To extricate itself from this compromise, it requires a regular *volte-face;* and this *volte-face* is the brusque transformation of tadpole into froglet which we call metamorphosis. (Fig. 8, 10–12.)

In this apparently simple phenomenon which occurs, unregarded, uncounted millions of times before our eyes each summer, we have in reality a most complex and delicately-adjusted set of processes. Think for a moment of all that it involves. The limbless tadpole must grow limbs, but at the same time must rid itself of tail. The machinery for water-breathing must be discarded, and replaced by one for air-breathing. The skin must be altered to fit it for land life: *inter alia*, means must be provided to keep it moist against the danger of desiccation. In the water, its weight was negligible: in air, that will no longer be so. Mr. Wells and other scientific romancers have made great play with the difference in weight which would be experienced on the moon by an inhabitant of earth: but the extent of the change of weight undergone by every tadpole which successfully turns into a frog is even greater.

Then the digestive system must be remodelled to suit a flesh diet instead of one predominantly vegetable: the horny jaws thrown off, true teeth grown, the intestine's long coils shortened, the liver and pancreas altered.

All these and other changes must all conspire to take effect at the same time.

Till well into the present century, the *how* of all this was still obscure. Uhlenhuth had shown that when organs which showed characteristic changes at metamorphosis were grafted from one tadpole to another of different age, they underwent transformation at the same time as their host, not at the time at which they would have changed in their original owner. Some general influence must then be permeating the whole body at the time of transformation, synchronising the changes in the several organs.

A little later, Gudernatsch discovered what this influence actually was. He had been much impressed by the then recent discoveries concerning the powers of the ductless glands in adult life, and felt that they must assuredly have equally striking powers over the course of development. The first animals with which he experimented were fish larvae. Regiments of these were taken and fed on preparations of all the different ductless glands and other organs. The work went on for a whole season—and was entirely negative so far as any visible effect upon rate or mode of development. Gudernatsch was discouraged. But instead of relinquishing the attempt, as many men would have done, he persevered. This time he used tadpoles; and this time he achieved success.

In one of the dozen or so of differently-dieted cultures which he had started, he noticed after a few days all the signs of impending metamorphosis, and, after a few days more, a metamorphosis precocious but complete. I once had the good fortune of a talk with him, and he told me how he hardly liked to believe what he saw, and how he repeated the experiment time and time again until there was no room for doubt.

The culture in which precocious metamorphosis took place was the culture fed on a preparation of thyroid gland. In that experiment Gudernatsch not only made probable what has since been abundantly confirmed, that the thyroid is the chief agent in the transformation of tadpole to frog, but laid the foundations of a whole new branch of knowledge —the accurate study of the effects of the ductless glands upon the processes of growth and development.

The way in which the thyroid regulates the tadpole's development is as follows: In the new-hatched tadpole the thyroid is not yet active; and it does not become active for a few weeks. Once it has started, however, it appears to grow rather faster than the rest of the body, so that its relative bulk and the concentration of its secretion within the body will be gradually increasing, since it is continually discharging its secretion into the blood. At first, most of the tissues appear to be insensitive to the secretion: but there is one which responds immediately, and that is the tissue of the limb-buds. If tadpoles are operated upon at an early stage and their thyroids removed, their limbs will grow, it is true, but exceedingly slowly. The presence of the normal thyroid within the body will cause them to grow at a moderate rate, while the addition of an excess of thyroid from outside will make them grow abnormally fast.

It seems probable that here the thyroid does one thing and one only—it regulates the *rate* at which the undifferentiated tissue of the limb-buds shall grow. On the other hand, the differentiation of the limbs, the appearance of fingers and toes upon them, the genesis of their skeleton, skin, and muscles, all this seems to be determined mainly by the amount of growth which they have undergone, so that the thyroid in this case would only bring about differentiation indirectly, by causing more rapid growth. If so, the thyroid would only be acting in the way common to most controlling factors in the animal organism; it would be altering the rate or extent of some independent process. For instance, the ventricle of the frog's heart has its own independent rate of beat when isolated. But in the intact animal this independent rate is all the time being speeded up by the faster-beating sinus venosus; and this in its turn can have its rate either slowed down or accelerated by different parts of the nervous system, through the vagus and the sympathetic respectively.

However, there do exist processes which will not occur at all unless some regulating substance is present in a certain concentration, and in the tadpole's metamorphosis the destruction of the tail and gills are such processes. For them to begin, it is needful not merely that some thyroid secretion should be circulating in the body, but that it should reach a certain definite concentration, a certain ' threshold value.' So it comes about that the destruction of the tail and gills does not start immediately that the thyroid becomes active (which would of course be highly inconvenient), but is put off for several months after this event. So too it comes about that tadpoles with thyroids removed will never metamorphose at all, but will continue to grow in tadpole form to sizes unheard-of in normal batrachian annals.

But it is not only thyroid substance which will accelerate metamorphosis. Iodine will do so as well, whether given as food or simply in solution in the water. The acceleration thus produced, however, is not nearly so great or so explosive as that which can be brought about by thyroid. The reason for this is that iodine, in the normal circumstances of tadpole existence, seems to be a limiting factor for the development of the thyroid and the manufacture of its secretion (which, as is well known, is largely composed of iodine, an element which elsewhere in the body is very sparingly present). Normally, that is to say, the infinitesimal amounts of iodine which exist in water and in plants are only sufficient to allow the tadpole to build up its thyroid at a certain slow rate of speed: give it more iodine, up even to the point at which the iodine becomes harmful, and the rate at which active thyroid secretion is formed becomes accelerated.

That is an object-lesson in limiting values, and in the extreme importance which may be assigned in the animal economy to substances existing in but the barest traces in nature.

This same substance, iodine, has the same limiting value in regard to the human thyroid. In the so-called goitre belt of the United States it has been shown that the enlargement of the thyroid, which is characteristic of the disease, is due to a futile attempt of the gland to compensate by over-production for the absence of iodine in the food, and therefore in the gland secretion. We are reminded of the Irishwoman who sold apples: she sold each pound at a loss, but managed, she said, to make a living by selling so many. We know what her eventual fate must have been; and so too chemical bankruptcy is the fate of the deluded thyroids that work so hard to increase its turnover but has no profit (in hard cash—otherwise iodine) to show for it. Iodine, administered regularly, even if in what seems infinitesimal traces, will cure the condition altogether.

Thus the amount of iodine in the water and the rate of growth of the thyroid relative to the body determine the time in the frog's life history at which the transformation from water to land shall take place. The specific reaction between thyroid secretion and tadpole tissues determines the transformation itself; the quantitative relations determine its precise moment.

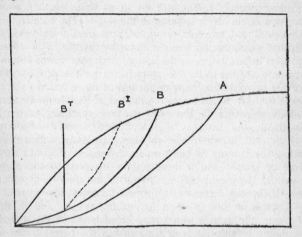

Fig. 9.—Diagram of effect of relative rate of thyroid-growth upon time of metamorphosis in tadpoles. The upper curve represents general growth; the lower curves represent thyroid-growth on a scale such that metamorphosis will occur when they intersect the upper curve.

    A. Late metamorphosis: *e.g.* Bull-frog.

    B. Early metamorphosis: *e.g.* Common Frog.

    B^I. Precocious metamorphosis due to administration of iodine. (Dotted line curve.)

    BT. Effect of thyroid administration: the concentration of the thyroid substance is at once raised above the value necessary for metamorphosis.

These ductless glands, with their internal secretions, have been found responsible for many vital processes which in past years puzzled physiologists.

If the tadpole's metamorphosis has afforded an excellent example of their effect upon long-continued processes of development, the colour-change of the adult frog gives us an instance of their importance for quick-acting but transitory physiological actions.

Frogs may be found of very various shades of colour, from a blotched yellow, through green and brown, almost to black; but it is not every one who is aware that all this range is within the capacity of a single individual. Put one frog in the dark with plenty of water, and another on a white background in the light in drier surroundings: at the end of a few hours the one will be nearly black, the other light greenish-yellow.

Not for years merely, but for decades, the explanation of this trivial fact eluded science. The tale is not without interest for the history of science, for it illustrates how the discovery of a new principle, albeit often of extreme simplicity, will at once bring order into confusion. Until comparatively recent times, the only agency known capable of bringing about rapid and transitory changes in animals was the nervous system. One after another, biologists attacked the problem of amphibian colour-change with the conviction that they would find a nervous mechanism behind it. What is more, most of them succeeded in demonstrating such a mechanism; but unfortunately their results were in mutual contradiction !

The idea that the blood might be the vehicle of another controlling mechanism, in the form of chemical substances circulating along its vessels, does not, you must confess, present any great difficulties to the imagination. Yet since Claude Bernard introduced physiology to the general idea of internal secretion, the whole field lay practically fallow until Bayliss and Starling, with the experiments on *secretin*, the hormone which makes the pancreas secrete, gave to the term internal secretion a more precise connotation, and started a new branch of biology.

Thus armed with a new principle, the most important new tool which she could possess, biology found the frog's colour-changes susceptible of a simple explanation. They depended on the secretion of the pituitary gland. This is a small gland at the base of the brain, partly formed in the embryo from an ingrowth from the roof of the mouth, partly from an outpushing from the brain itself. The ingrowth from the mouth divides into several parts; one of these, called the intermediate lobe from its position in the human gland, pours into the blood a secretion which has been experimentally shown to cause frogs to become darker. When injected into a frog, it is absorbed into the blood, circulates throughout the system, and when it comes to the skin, acts upon the special pigment-cells which are there to be found. These cells consist of a central body with much-branched arms, together with a certain quantity of dark pigment. When there is no pituitary secretion in the blood, as, for example, when the gland has been cut out of a frog, all the pigment is clumped in the central body: but when much pituitary secretion is present, the pigment is caused to stream out into the branches, thus covering a much greater visible area and giving the animal its dark colour.

Further, the pituitary gland itself is under nervous control. When, for instance, the animal is on a light background, the stimuli to the eyes are relayed as impulses to the pituitary, forcing it to shut down production; this of course has the result of making the animal lighter and lighter in colour as the available supplies of the secretion in the blood are used up.

Here, as you see, nervous system and ductless glands co-operate, with nervous system in ultimate control. The brain is here like the manager's office in some big business concern. It gives its orders to the pituitary, which we may symbolise as a private printing works and clerical staff, and this subordinate branch of the business floods the customers—the body and its cells—with circulars. The circulars travel into every street, are dropped in at every door; but, as in real life, only a fraction of the recipients take any action as a result.

The relation between the thyroid's action on metamorphosis and the nervous system is much more obscure. One very curious fact we know: that tadpoles can be kept eight or ten days under narcosis, immovable, with all the higher centres out of action, by means of anaesthetics such as urethane; and yet that if they are previously treated with thyroid, such anaesthetised animals will undergo precocious metamorphosis just as rapidly as normal ones, waking up from their sleep to find themselves transmogrified, with no familiar tail, but two pairs of brand-new and unfamiliar legs !

We also know that the thyroid is capable of great compensatory adjustment to changes in the outer world. As the simplest instance of this, there is the fact that if very young tadpoles, in which the thyroid is just forming, are given extraneous thyroid substance, their own gland remains very much underdeveloped; in other words, the stimulus of having to provide the amount of secretion that is normally demanded by the body is one of the conditions for the full development of the normal gland. Even in the obscure life of organs within the body, work is one of the conditions for the attainment of full potentiality.

This compensation also operates with regard to temperature. Tadpoles brought up at unusually low temperatures show unusually large thyroids, and *vice versâ*. In a cold-blooded animal, of course, activity in general is greater with increase of temperature. The thyroid is, *inter alia*, a regulator of the general chemical activity. Inject a man, a dog, or a tadpole with a little thyroid, and his metabolism, as measured by the amount of oxygen consumed and carbon dioxide given off, will rise considerably. It thus appears that when temperature raises the general activity of the tadpole's body, less call is made upon the thyroid, and so it tends to shut down, and to grow less rapidly than it would normally do. Thus this power of compensatory activity possessed by the gland would have as effect that the activities of tadpoles are not raised as much by heat as they would be if the thyroid had no compensatory power, nor so much depressed by cold. In other words, changes in the outer world are damped down, so to speak, before they affect the activities of the body as a whole, and we get a first approximation to that internal regulation of the body, that high degree of independence of outer change, which has become complete in regard to temperature in the ' warm-blooded ' mammals and birds. But to what degree all this power of regulation of the thyroid is in its turn regulated by the nervous system, of that we are as yet almost wholly ignorant.

However, both of our endocrine examples illustrate another interesting fact of general application. I have so far only mentioned that metamorphosis can be brought about by thyroid, colour-darkening by pituitary, without specifying anything as to what kind of thyroid, or what kind of pituitary.

The fact is remarkable. *Any* kind of thyroid will bring about the tadpole's metamorphosis, even thyroid from an animal never becomes terrestrial like a fish, or one which has put all trace of metamorphosis behind it like a sheep or a dog. And similarly any kind of pituitary will cause frogs to grow dark in colour, whether it comes from a bird or mammal which cannot change its own colour, or from a chameleon in which colour-change does exist, but is not under pituitary control.

In other words, the substances produced by the thyroid and the pituitary are chemically identical or at least essentially similar throughout the vertebrate series, while the effects they produce may vary enormously from one type to another.

A good example of this variation lies ready to our hand in the metamorphosis of different kinds of amphibians. The more primitive tailed amphibians like newt and sala-mander exhibit a much less violent transformation than the tadpole. Their limbs have been well formed almost throughout their aquatic life, their tail is not got rid of when they leave the water for land. This is due to the fact, easily demonstrated by experiment, that in them neither limb-tissue nor tail-tissue is in the least responsive to thyroid secretion; during the evolution of frogs and toads from their tailed forbears, one of the chief changes that has come about has been the alteration of these tissues so that the one responds by growth, the other by degeneration, to the presence of thyroid substance in the blood.

Precisely how this has been achieved we do not know. But it is a good object-lesson of a very simple but important fact—the fact that if it takes two to make a quarrel, so it takes two to make an endocrine effect, namely, the internal secretion and the tissue sensitised to it. This should warn us against that seductive type of speculation which would have us find a single ductless gland exerting the same kind of effect throughout the entire series of vertebrated animals, and wishing, for instance, to ascribe to the over-productivity of the same gland such a phenomenon as bull-dogging of the jaw wherever it occurs, be it in salmon, goldfish, pug, bull-dog, pekinese, abnormal calves, or human beings. It may be so: but it is just as likely not to be so. Why, even in the course of a single life-time a structure may come under the control of two different ductless glands. The back fin of the newt is present in the newt tadpole; and also in the adult durings its watery sojourn in the breeding season. In the first period, thyroid injection causes its absorption, in the second it does not.

But the ductless glands have still other lessons of very general application to teach us. Their origin, both in the individual and in the race, is often strange and interesting in the extreme.

For one thing, it is often double. We have already seen this for the pituitary—half from brain, half from roof of mouth. It is true also for the adrenal, that little yellowish gland we carry close to our kidney, whose central core is made of cells which have migrated out of the spinal cord, its outer layers of cells from a ridge which seems to be a continuation of the same embryonic rudiment which gives rise to the reproductive organs. What is more, these two parts are originally quite distinct: in fish there are two wholly separate sets of organs corresponding to the two parts of the mammalian gland.

The same is true of the mammalian thyroid apparatus. The parathyroids are small glands whose very name shows their close proximity to the thyroid—in the mammal. Indeed in many mammals the parathyroids may be entirely embedded in the thyroid. In lower vertebrates, however, the two are quite separate. The parathyroid has quite different functions from the thyroid, one of them being to regulate the calcium supply within the body.

It is assuredly no accident that this unification of originally separate rudiments or organs has taken place so often in the system of the ductless glands; but of the reasons therefor we are almost wholly in the dark: I can only give you the facts for what they are worth—another challenge to human curiosity and intelligence.

If, however, we understand little of the meaning of the end-result, we can sometimes discover much that is significant about the origin of these organs.

The thyroid arises in the embryo frog as a down-growth from the floor of the hinder part of the mouth. The original connecting stalk disappears, and the deeper part becomes transformed into glandular tissue. That does not seem to help us much. But there is one animal now in existence whose development supplies the missing clue. That animal is the lamprey.

The lamprey is one of those living fossils so precious to the zoologist. It is built on a plan which undoubtedly was that of the ancestors of all higher vertebrates—fully a vertebrate, but not yet truly a fish. For instance, it still lacks limbs, it still lacks jaws, it still lacks teeth. Its skull is not yet a true skull, but a mere platform on which the brain rests, and its backbone is only a series of small struts not yet united together.

It, however, possesses a thyroid gland like all other vertebrated animals; but this thyroid arises in a remarkable way.

The lamprey starts independent life as a larva, the so-called ammocoete or lampern, which, instead of being carnivorous, lives in the mud of rivers and extracts the microscopic particles of organic debris therefrom. Part of its apparatus for so doing is the endostyle, a pocket in the floor of the mouth which passes out a sticky mucus it has secreted, in which the food particles in the water may be entangled. This method of feeding and the whole apparatus for its execution is found in the same form in the primitive animal known as the amphioxus or lancelet, and in the whole degenerate group of tunicates. In them it is retained throughout life; but in the ammocoete at the moment of metamorphosis the endostyle degenerates together with the rest of the mud-feeding apparatus,—save that a small part of it is retained, and differentiates into the thyroid gland of the adult lamprey.

This economical process, whereby an organ which has lost its original use through the animal's change of life, becomes converted into another organ with wholly different function, has been repeated again and again in the course of evolution, but nowhere more prominently than in the ductless glands. For instance, the pineal gland (though doubtless never the seat of the soul, as Descartes asserted!) was once one of a pair of upwardly-directed eyes. The parathyroids are budded off from the gill-slits a little before these degenerate in the embryo (or, in tadpoles, at metamorphosis), preparatory to land life. The thymus, too, that gland in the neck, one of whose functions has just been discovered to be the control of the egg-envelopes, arises in connection with the gill-slits; and seems to have been built out of the remains of the nephridia or primitive kidneys of amphioxus.

Sometimes a purely temporary function is undertaken by an organ which must degenerate during individual development. At the tadpole's metamorphosis, the fore-limbs, which have previously been concealed under the gill-cover, burst through. It was first of all thought that the mere pressure of the growing limb caused the perforation. But it was found that the perforation appeared just as well if the limb-bud had been removed in earlier stages! Quite recently it has been discovered that the perforation was brought about by the tadpole's gills when they had reached a certain stage in their degeneration: graft a piece of metamorphosing gill under the skin of the back, and perforation will occur above the graft. In this case, only local action occurs, and the ' organ of internal secretion ' derived from the gill is of briefest duration instead of persisting throughout life. Nevertheless, the example serves well to illustrate an early stage in the genesis of a true ductless gland by the utilisation of by-products of development.

. . . . .

I have wandered far afield from the frogs of my boyish memories, trapped by their own instincts in the sunken tank; but I am now going to return to them for a fresh start.

What first attracted our attention to them was the noise they made, a chorus of croaking, harsh and raucous from the frogs, soft and musical from the toads. That, as you know, is all spring music; but it is music which is found in almost every species of frog or toad in existence. In our northern climate, this frog-music is a quiet little affair; but in more southern countries it provides one of the memorable sounds of nature. In France they have five or six species of batrachians against our three; and in the spring in marshy parts of the country they sing to such purpose that under the *ancien régime* one of the tasks imposed upon the peasants was to beat the waters of the ponds at night so that the frogs would hush and let the nobility slumber.

In the Southern States of America there are grass-frogs, and leopard-frogs, and bull-frogs, and toads, and tree-toads; and the voices of some of them are far more powerful than ours. In the spring a few wet days will fill the prairie pools, and the pools will fill with toads and frogs, and then the evenings and nights will be full of sound—a continuous sound, rising and falling like the sound of the sea. For three years I lived in Texas, and when I left, I think that manifestation of Nature which I most missed was the sound of the frogs in spring. Others too who have lived in the south have told me that they felt the same.

What is this sound and its meaning? It is produced with the aid of large resonators, in the shape of distensible pockets

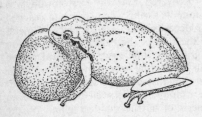

of skin under the throat or on either side of the neck. This is in the males only, for the females do not croak. A small male tree-frog croaking, with expanded pouches bigger than his own head, is a never-to-be-forgotten spectacle.

FIG. 10.—Male tree-frog croaking with distended 'resonator.'

And the purpose and function of the croaking? The function seems to be simply that of recognition between the sexes, the females being guided to their mates by the sound. 'The frog he would a-wooing go—"Heigho!"' said Anthony Rowley'—and 'croak, croak' says the frog himself.

In this respect too the frog is in a sense at an intermediate level of animal evolution. The lowest multicellular animals shed their gametes or reproductive cells free into the water, leaving chance to do the rest; at most, a certain synchronisation of the shedding on the part of a large number of individuals is achieved in some cases, probably by some chemical stimulus of one individual on the rest, in others apparently altogether under the regulation of outer influences such as the seasons or the tides. Before the evolution of complex sense-organs and still more of brains behind those sense-organs, anything more elaborate would have been useless and impossible.

At the other extreme we have creatures like birds with perfected eyes and ears and brains so elaborate as to permit of a complex emotional life. Reproduction has become so much more complex that fertilisation must be internal, and an act of pairing is therefore essential. Furthermore, no longer is the liberation of the gametes a mere reflex action, nor yet a simple instinct, but is under the control of the highest centres, and demands the proper adjustment of the emotional system before it can be carried out. One of the main functions of the strange and beautiful dances and displays which are to be seen in birds at courting-time is undoubtedly to tune the emotions of the two birds of a pair, male and female, to the same key simultaneously and so facilitate mating. Even among birds, however, evolution has here and there gone on to a higher stage. In grebes and herons and other birds in which the sexes are alike and both indulge in elaborate display, the display often seems to be performed for its own sake, without special stimulative function. The only function it can then be supposed to keep is that of linking the pair together throughout the breeding season by emotional bonds; this may well have its biological value, since in all such species, both sexes help in incubation and in attending to the young, and anything which binds the pair more closely together for the good of the family is a racial blessing. This emancipation of courtship and display from a merely stimulative function has of course in man reached up higher on to new levels, and out wider so as to commingle with other parts of the emotional life—higher and wider than in any other creature.

But of all this in the frog there is no trace. The actual mating is still a merely or essentially physiological process, not a psychological one. However, the sexes must be brought together with as little waste as possible; brain and sense-organs have been developed to a comparatively high pitch to subserve the general functions of catching prey and escaping from enemies—they can be brought under call to supply this new demand.

In part, the male frog's croaking is like the male spider's dancing or still better the male fiddler-crab's statuesque poses with enormous claw uplifted—it is an advertisement of his maleness. But in part it is an advertisement of the breeding grounds, a boosting of choice real estate; and in this frogs foreshadow song-birds, whose song is a sky-sign read by other birds according to their sex—to other males, a warning to trespassers, to the females, an advertisement of home and husband.

In any event, the amphibian's croaking is interesting from yet another biological aspect. It was the first vocal music that life brought to birth. No doubt insects had been deliberately producing their chirpings, trillings, and hummings before fish ever left the water; but they are instrumentalists all, making zithers of their legs or fiddles of their wings.

The land vertebrates offered life two new possibilities of sound-production—the pipe with reed, in the shape of the windpipe and vocal chords; and, in the mouth, a cavity communicating with the pipe and alterable in shape. The first gave the possibility of varying pitch, the second of altering the type and form of the sounds: and so it is sober truth to say that only through some humble beginning such as that which the croaking frog gives us in spring, could bird song and human song and speech have come into existence.

Again, the frog's croak is a reminder of the strange part which sex has played in the history of life—a part which to the eye of detachment sometimes seems fantastic.

Let us follow the steps of this history, and see how each has led on inevitably but unexpectedly to new. The first step of all was the establishment of sex itself, the union of two separate cells into one. Of the origin and cause of this primal process we are almost wholly ignorant. We merely know that it is probably not a necessary function of life, since it has so far not been found at all, in spite of determined search, in the whole great group of bacteria. Once it was established, however, it came immediately to have a new biological significance. It made possible the recombination in one strain of new favourable mutations that had originated in separate strains, and so facilitated evolutionary change. (Very possibly the absence of this help to variation is compensated for in the bacteria by their prodigious rate of multiplication.)

Fusion is first between like cells, or cells so like that they are indistinguishable by the eye. And so we have the paradox that sex, in its origins, does not imply what we are accustomed to think of as its essential, namely, two different sexes. But the unescapable law of economy sees to it that the economical principle of the division of labour shall have full play in sex as in other departments of life. And so the active mobile male cell is differentiated from the passive female cell with its reserve stores of material. This primary difference gradually is thrown back on to more and more of the rest of the organism. First the reproductive organs alone are sexed: then their ducts; then the instincts of male and female; then come the secondary sexual characters serving the functions of display and courtship; and those serving the nourishment and protection of the next generation. With the development of long-continued care of the young, the rôles of the two parents may again diverge; and from this the divergence spreads until a sexual difference may arise in respect of all the everyday businesses of feeding and of escape from enemies. Finally, in man, where the barriers between the different compartments of the mental organism have been more broken down than in other creatures, any emotion is able to play its part in colouring any experience, and so sex spreads through the whole mind, and is one of the great pillars on which its higher life is built.

. . . .

So the race of frogs continues, fixed it would seem irrevocably in an evolutionary half-way house, a peculiar and specialised manifestation of life, risen far above life's primitive estate, and exhibiting many adumbrations of her higher achievements. Each year they mate, and generate new frog-lives, and die. Their whole existence is delicately regulated by the never-ending pressure of circumstance, to the world around, and attuned to what appears to be its only end—its own adequate performance.

Its only end, but not its only function: for each organism performs many functions in respect of other organisms, whether as food for this one, or in keeping this other up to full pitch by constant pursuit. And here to-day the frog has even been performing a function in the sphere of the intellect, in providing a text for my biological sermon !

What we know of modern physics assures us that to separate any particle of matter from the rest of the universe can be only either an intellectual trick or a practical approximation. Matter is in the ultimate analysis nothing but a vast number of centres of activity. The activity diminishes as we pass away from the centre, like the wave from a stone's splash; it increases as we pass toward the centre until finally the forces at work are enormous, the remaining core becomes what we call impenetrable, and we speak of it as a material unit. But in reality the influences of the activities of all the units interpenetrate in the one cosmos.

So it is in the mental kingdom. It is impossible to pose a question without a reverberation which raises up further questions, one after the other, till, if we are willing in the pursuit, we find we have started a stir in the whole organism of knowledge.

Let my brief and incomplete words to-day at least serve as a reminder of this fact, and as an appeal to teachers not to allow themselves or their pupils to become so smothered with facts and details and the requirements of examining boards that they lose sight of this reality, and with it the light of intellectual day.

THE TADPOLE

EVERYONE knows the look of frog spawn. The sticky, tough coverings of jelly bind the eggs into a coherent mass. They serve not only as protective and distasteful covering, but also as condenser of the sun's heat upon the living specks of black which they contain. It is these which are the real eggs. When first laid, they are about three millimetres in diameter, black above and whitish below. Microscopic examination, even by the most elaborate technique, reveals comparatively little within them. There is a so-called nucleus —a special vesicle with a definite membrane of its own— lying in the axis, nearer to the black pole. The rest is occupied by the living cell-protoplasm or cytoplasm, and its non-living contents—yolk, fat, and animal starch or glycogen— which are to serve for the nourishment of the embryo before it can shift for itself. The fat is uniformly distributed; the yolk (by far the most abundant of the three) becomes more concentrated towards the white or ' vegetative ' pole, the glycogen more concentrated towards the black or 'animal' pole.

At the moment of their extrusion, the eggs had spermatozoa shed over them by the male, and these sperms effected the eggs' fertilisation. Each egg was penetrated by one of the millions of tiny lashing living organisms (once penetration had started, a change occurred in the egg's surface preventing the entry of any further male cells), the compressed sperm-' head ' swelled up till it became a nucleus like that of the egg, and the two, becoming apposed, united into one. This union of nuclei from father and mother is essential act of fertilisation. The nucleus contains the chromosomes, which in their turn carry the factors or genes determining inheritance. Thus fertilisation brings about the combination of one maternal and one paternal set or pack of chromosomes and therefore of hereditary constitutions.

The second, but in a sense subsidiary function of fertilisation is to set development going; the egg, which if left to itself would have died without further change, a few hours after fertilisation divides into two, and upon this follow all the other changes of development in sequence. This function I call a subsidiary one, not because it is less important, but because it can be imitated by other means The unfertilised frog's egg, for instance, can be caused to develop if it is pricked with a fine glass needle previously

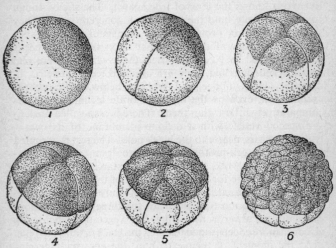

FIG. 11.—Early Segmentation of the Frog's Egg.
(1) Fertilised egg; (2) 2-cell stage; (3) 4-cell stage; (4) 8-cell stage;
(5) 8- to 16-cell stage; (6) early blastula.

dipped in frog's blood, and from this act of artificial parthenogenesis can arise adult frogs, healthy although fatherless.

But normally it is a fertilised egg which is the start of the new individual. The problem of development is to understand how it is possible that this simple motionless sphere can within a few days give rise to a tadpole, a creature capable of swimming, seeing, hearing, smelling, feeling, feeding, growing, and the rest, and, for all its littleness and insignificance, possessing an organisation of no mean complexity, with heart, muscles, brain, sense-organs, stomach, digestive glands, kidneys, ductless secretions, protective skin, and skeleton. Not only that, but we have to find out how this tadpole comes to leave the water at the right time, and at the same moment become transformed into a frog by undergoing just those changes which fit it for terrestrial life.

The average man takes it for granted that the frog's egg shall grow up just as it does, in apparently inevitable rightness of development, into the full-grown animal. Why should one trouble one's head with such everyday problems as the genesis of pollywogs? But it is just the everyday problems which are so important, because they have such universality of application. And if we could understand, even in broad lines, how a frog grows from its egg, we should possess the key to a new domain of nature.

First, however, we must know what we have to explain; description before analysis. And although any text-book of embryology will give us all the description we want, I may be pardoned if I run quickly through the essentials.

The first phase of development is known as segmentation, because the single-celled egg segments into a large number—perhaps a couple of thousand—of small cells. At the same time a cavity—the segmentation cavity—appears in the mass of cells, or blastula as it is now called. No growth takes place; and the only differentiation consists in the fact that the cells towards the white yolky pole are larger as well as more yolk-laden. It is generally concluded that the main function of segmentation is simply to divide up the unwieldy egg-cell into living bricks of convenient size for the future building. (Fig. 11.)

Next come what are technically known as gastrulation and germ-layer formation, which we may characterise as the laying-down of the first (and roughest imaginable) ground-plan of the future animal. At one point, just below the equator of the egg, at the junction of dark and light cells, a little crack appears. This marks the middle of the future back of the tadpole. The cells just above this crack must be in active growth, for they push downwards as a double fold over the white cells, which at the same time can, by appropriate methods, be seen to stream slowly in towards and under the crack. Meanwhile the crack spreads round to the sides, and wherever it becomes visible the same process of overgrowth of yolk begins; it becomes crescentic, horseshoe-shaped, and finally closes to a circle: the circle decreases in size and at length closes to a tiny aperture. The effect is to cover the large white cells by a double fold of the small black cells, and to tuck more and more of the yolk away into the interior. The circle enclosed by the crack is called the blastopore; and the first part to appear is consequently its dorsal lip, followed by the lateral lips, and then the ventral lip.

The space between the double fold and the yolk is the rudiment of the future digestive tube—the first organ to be formed in all higher animals. This dilates at its interior end and eventually sqeezes the segmentation cavity out of existence.

The outer layer of the double fold is the outer germ-layer or ectoderm, from which will arise epidermis, sense organs, and nervous system: the inner layer and the yolk mass together constitute the endoderm, destined to form lungs, digestive tube with its glands, and one or two other organs: and meanwhile between the two a third layer is split off as the mesoderm, from which will develop all the other systems of the body—skeleton, muscles, blood and blood-vessels, kidneys, and reproductive organs. The two splits become continued round the whole embryo, so that it is entirely divided into the three germ-layers.

The next phase can best be characterised as that of primary differentiation, or, if you will, of the formation of organ-systems.

Externally it is begun by the elongation of the embryo; at the same time along the back there appears a thickened plate of tissue, the medullary plate, from which the future nervous system is to be formed. The sides of this plate grow up as medullary folds, the centre sinks in, the folds meet, the epidermis grows over them, and the plate is thus converted into a hollow tube—the neural tube.

The front region of this tube is enlarged, and will become the brain. It is divided into definite parts. First of all fore, mid, and hind brain are marked off. Then from the fore-brain a swelling arises, the optic vesicle, main rudiment of the future eye. Meanwhile the future 'nose' comes into being as a shallow olfactory pit, and the ear as a hollow auditory sac derived from the epidermis. Below the nervous system arises the first embryonic skeleton, an unsegmented rod called the notochord, and on either side of this the mesoderm becomes arranged into a series of little blocks called somites, the future trunk-muscles. In the mesoderm round the gut a split has occurred, which enlarges later to form the main body-cavity or coelom. From this cavity at its front end grow out a series of hollow funnels, rather like miniature tobacco-pipes. With their outer ends (the pipe-stems) these form a tube, which grows back and comes to open into the hindmost part of the intestine. The funnels will constitute the kidney of the tadpole, the tube the kidney duct or ureter. In the mass of yolk cells in the floor of the gut a hollow is excavated—the rudiment of the liver. And from the pharynx or region just behind the mouth, pockets grow out towards the side of the head, finally fusing with little ingrowths from the skin and so putting pharynx in communication with the exterior: these are the gill-slits, which are present at some stage of the life-history in every vertebrate from lowest fish to highest mammal.

A collection of mesoderm cells below the pharynx unites and organises itself into a tube: the tube bends into an S-shape, divides itself into four sections, and begins to beat: it is the heart. Similar scattered mesoderm cells in other parts have also organised themselves into tubes, and these eventually join up with each other and with the heart to form the blood-vessels. Any cells contained within these tubes develop into blood-cells.

Meanwhile externally the blastopore, after temporary closure, has reopened into the hind end of the gut, to form the anus; and above it the tail starts to grow out. A depression becomes visible on the lower surface of the head and breaks through into the pharynx as the mouth; on either side of it arise the rudiments of the two suckers by which the new-hatched tadpole will attach itself. And on the ridges between the gill-slits appear little outgrowths which will later branch and grow to form the gills.

But at the start these organs are only laid down as in a plan—their positions are marked out, their material is delimited, but they do not *work*. For this, the individual cells of which they are composed must become differentiated. At the start, the cells of all the different tissues of the body are still extremely similar, still in what we may call the embryonic condition. They are rounded, or more or less cubical, or polyhedral, according to their mode of aggregation; but show no special distinguishing structure. It is only after the laying down of the nervous system and the blocking out of its chief parts that its component cells send out fibres and become in any real sense nerve-cells; only after the separation of the future muscle-segments that their cells elongate and develop contractile fibrils; and so forth.

Thus for each organ a period of rough form-differentiation is followed by a tissue-differentiation, involving detailed cell-form and proper function; and although, when the whole body is considered, the two processes overlap very considerably, yet there is a stage where only form-differentiation is proceeding, and this is followed by one where tissue-differentiation is preponderatingly at work.

The close of this latter phase brings the embryo to a condition in which it can shift for itself. It hatches out as the larva we call a tadpole, and new processes begin.

In one respect, we may say that growth is the chief characteristic of this new phase; for the animal, which hitherto has been living on its self-contained reserves, soon begins to take up foreign matter and build it into its own tissues; and, although quite considerable changes of form and function do take place during the larval period, yet they do not produce any change so striking as the hundred-fold multiplication of the animal's bulk which is brought about by growth.

The main morphological changes externally visible in larval life are the overgrowth of the gills by the gill-cover, and the development of the limbs. After a small increase of size has taken place, a flap of skin grows back from the side of the head to enclose the outside of the gill-slit region in a gill-chamber. Water taken in at the mouth and forced out through the gill-slits now passes into this gill-chamber, and thence to the exterior by a little aperture which remains on the left side.

At a rather later stage, the rudiments of the hind limbs are to be seen as two buds of undifferentiated tissue close to the anus. These gradually grow and differentiate until they are quite respectable miniatures of the adult legs.

Meanwhile the fore-limbs also have begun to form, but they are concealed beneath the gill-cover.

Another interesting point is correlated with the relative importance of growth. In the previous stages, change had been rapid and kaleidoscopic: each phase no sooner arose than it melted into the next, like a dissolving view. Now the same general form (especially once the gill-cover has appeared) continues with slight modifications over considerable periods of time.

Of the organs which were differentiated in the final embryonic phases, the blood-system was one: and the blood-system is of paramount importance for our present purpose, because, once formed, its contained blood bathes every tissue of the body, and so constitutes a common 'internal environment' for the whole organism. The nervous system is of importance for the same general reason— because the nerves which pass out from and into the central nervous organs come to connect every part of the body with a common exchange and so again provide not only a structural basis for individuality, but a mechanism for constant co-ordination and regulation. Neither of these conditions was realised in the embryo. Accordingly the parts of the organism in the embryo can and must be more isolated from each other, both chemically and physically, must be less co-ordinated, than the parts of the larva or the adult.

Into the blood-system are poured the most various substances from different tissues of the body. For our present purpose the most important are the so-called 'internal secretions.' These are the produce of the ductless glands— secreting organs, like the thyroid or pituitary, which discharge their secretions entirely into the blood. By means of these special substances, new possibilities of chemical regulation are provided; we shall see in the sequel to what use they are turned.

Finally, when the tadpole has reached a certain size, profound form-changes once more set in. The fore-limbs burst through the gill-cover. The body-shape changes, the eyes protrude, the blackish skin becomes lighter and blotchy, and the tail begins to shrink. In the space of a few days the tail has disappeared, the other changes have run to their limit, and the tadpole (though not without much loss of weight and a considerably heightened mortality-risk) is become a tiny frog.

Internally the changes have been as profound. The gills have shrunk to nothing, the gill-slits closed up, the long spiral gut of the mainly herbivorous tadpole has shortened to a fraction of its original length in preparation for the exclusively carnivorous habits of the frog. The skeleton of the tadpole is mainly cartilaginous: during metamorphosis, bone-formation is rapid, thus not only preparing the animal's framework for the greater strain it will have to contend with on the land, but also bringing about remarkable changes in form, especially in the skull. The brain also is profoundly modified, and there are important changes in liver and pancreas. The lungs become the main organ of respiration, and the character of the skin becomes adapted to terrestrial instead of aquatic existence.

Such a radical change in form accompanying a radical change in mode of life is called a metamorphosis; and with very few exceptions all amphibia metamorphose from an aquatic to a terrestrial existence. There are, however, many interesting differences of detail. As regards time, for instance, the bull-frog lives two years as a tadpole, the leopard-frog a full year, the ordinary English frog three to five months, some toads only six to eight weeks.

We shall often have occasion to supplement the knowledge we can derive from the frog with that from other species, particularly from the tailed amphibia—newts, salamanders, and the like—which are technically known as Urodeles.

On many grounds, these animals must be held to be less specialised, less modified during evolution from the ancestral form of amphibians, than the tailless Anura—the frogs and toads. In accordance with this, their larval form is much less unlike the adult, and their metamorphosis less violent and abrupt. For instance, the tail is not lost when they pass from water to land, but only the broad fin which borders it; and instead of the limbs appearing late in tadpole life, they are present from the first. Another primitive feature is that they have no gill-cover, the red feathery gills standing out unprotected on either side of the neck. We may say that just as a frog is on the whole more specialised for a land existence than is a newt, so is a frog tadpole more specialised for larval growth in water than a newt tadpole, the appearance of its aquatically-useless legs being delayed till the last possible moment.

Once the land has been safely escaladed, further development is mainly an affair of simple growth. Finally, after another two or three years, the sexual organs ripen, the animal becomes mature, and can reproduce its kind.

Thus the rate of change during development on the whole becomes slower and slower as time goes on. The bewildering complication of processes by which the single fertilised egg-cell generates the rudiments of all the future organs of the body is an affair of days. In a week the embryo becomes enough of a self-sufficing organism to hatch as a larva. In a month it has become a full-blown tadpole—in three or four, metamorphosis is accomplished—and from then on till the close of life there is very little change of function, and scarcely any change of form.

Thus far observation, whose main contribution is to provide the facts to be explained. These facts can perhaps best be summed up in one phrase—that development is what we call an *epigenetic* process—in other words that real increase of complexity, real differentiation, occur during its course.

But *how* is differentiation brought into being? That is one of the great problems of biology. Development is to the individual what evolution is to the race. Both are processes in the course of which something appears to be created out of nothing, or at least out of a something much less complex and elaborate. The psalmist summed it up in a sentence when he wrote, ' In thy book all my members were written, which in continuance were fashioned, when as yet there was none of them.' That is it—they are being fashioned; and yet they are not in existence. Creation is here made visible.

' In thy book all my members are written.' We can subscribe to that to-day as whole-heartedly as could its writer over two thousand years ago. We are sure, thanks to the patient labour of science, that all is written in the book of Nature, and, what is more, that it is written so that we men, if we take time and pains enough, can decipher it. The book is no longer to us the private and guarded secret of a divine Personage, but its pages are outspread in the existing world, and are guarded only by the passive secret of the language in which they are written. And so we have hope that even this process, which has seemed to many thinkers the most mysterious and unintelligible in the whole realm of reality, may yet be unravelled into order and intelligible sequence.

Much progress has been made in the last few decades towards a preliminary analysis of development. It is not much more than a hundred years ago that development was first shown to be truly epigenetic, and no mere unfolding of a performed miniature. It was Wolff, Goethe, Pander, von Baer who thus really founded the modern science of descriptive embryology, between the years 1780 and 1820. This science developed rapidly, and by a natural change became converted into comparative embryology as a result of the impetus given to all forms of comparative biology by Darwin.

But, although many theories as to the methods of development were advanced, very little progress was made in experimental analysis until the last decade of the nineteenth century. At this time zoologists, tired of theoretical polemics concerning the methods of evolution, and of unverifiable family trees whose shade proved unfavourable for more profitable crops, were turning to experimental work of all sorts and descriptions. In the field of embryology, Roux Driesch, Morgan, Wilson, and a host of others were the pioneers. The flood of enthusiasm continued unabated for some fifteen or twenty years, but was then largely diverted into other channels, such as genetics, although fine workers like Herbst, Spemann, Boveri, Conklin, Harrison, Brachet, and Jenkinson continued to give the major part of their attention to it.

The subject is now entering on a new phase. For one thing, the work, particularly of American biologists, upon the rôle of the ductless glands in the development of tadpoles is linking up classical physiology with the physiology of development. It has also, as has the splendid work of Goldschmidt on sex, emphasised the importance of bringing in time, of thinking in terms of relative rate of chemical processes for an understanding of developmental order. Then Spemann, going from triumph to triumph of technique,

has begun to lay clear to us the secret of the start of differentiation, while Harrison is doing the same for later stages.
Child, with his axial gradients, has at least given an intelligible
common basis to a whole mass of scattered facts in the
fields of regeneration, polarity, growth, embryology, and
physiology: and last but by no means least, Bateson, Correns,
Baur, Morgan, and the host of other workers in genetics
have shown us the basis from which development must
take its origin.

The individual frog begins its existence as a fertilised
egg. In this form it differs in the most profound ways from
its adult self. It is small or even minute: it consists of but
one cell instead of thousands, millions, or billions; instead
of organs and co-operating parts of the greatest diversity
and complexity it is a mere spherical mass of substance in
which the only differentiation visible is a gradation of the
materials of which it is composed, a stratification from one
pole towards the other, and, further, a distinction between
general protoplasm and nucleus.

But in spite of its lack of visible differentiation, we believe
with good reason that it possesses a hidden complexity.
The great majority at least of its hereditary factors or genes
are lodged in the nucleus; and we have every cause to believe
that what Morgan and his pupils have proved for the little
fly Drosophila holds good in essentials for other organisms—
to wit, that these factors exist not only in constant relative
quantity, but in a fixed position with reference to each
other. The genes, of which there are at least several hundred
and probably some thousands in the fly, are disposed in
order along the bodies we know as chromosomes, and,
since the chromosomes are self-reproducing, their sum
really represents one vast chemical unit, whose parts—the
separate genes—occupy a constant position in the whole,
just as do the atoms of a simple molecule. Sometimes one
of these units changes, owing to causes we do not yet understand; and the effect of this may be made visible as what
we call a mutation, which is inherited because the altered
gene now reproduces itself in its new form, and is inherited
in Mendelian fashion. For example one gene in Drosophila
when altered produces a dilution of the red colour of the
eye. A number of alterations in this one gene are known,

G

their effects grading from red through pink to white, each
' breeding true ' because self-reproducing. And this particular
gene has been tracked down to a particular position near on
end of the first or sex-determining chromosome. Another gene
in the same chromosome affects chiefly the colours of the body;
another the shape of the wings, others the general viability.

We thus know a good deal about the number, arrangement, and hereditary transmission of genes; and a good
deal about the visible differences in the adult with which
gene-alterations are correlated. But we know nothing or
next to nothing of all the intermediate steps—the method
by which the genes come to influence the characters: and
it is largely this with which developmental physiology will
in the long run be concerned. Meanwhile it must be confessed
that we are far removed from success in this task, and in
most cases must be content with a very preliminary analysis.

With these prolegomena we may now proceed to our
main task. First, then, the stage of segmentation. Oscar
Hertwig long ago, in 1897, following Balfour, enunciated
the rule that the nuclear spindle, at cell-division, elongated
in the direction of least resistance, and that this resistance
was partly determined by the mere size of the different
dimensions of a cell, partly by the quality of its contents,
yolk offering more resistance than living protoplasm: and
further that yolk slowed down the rate of division. This
serves to explain the observed sequence of divisions in the
frog—two meridional followed by a latitudinal and so forth,
and also the fact that the cells towards the animal pole are
smaller, cell-size gradually increasing towards the yolk-pole.

This was later verified experimentally. In the first place,
when eggs were made to segment under pressure, the furrows
continued to run meridionally until after the fourth division,
since the pressure had reduced the distance from animal
to vegetative side. Secondly, the deduction as to the influence
of yolk received a still more striking confirmation. When
rogs' eggs are violently centrifuged, the heavy yolk is driven
outwards. If the force applied is only moderate, the furrows
still cut right through the egg, though the vegetative cells
are larger than normal. But if the centrifuging is strong,
the concentration of dead yolk is so great at the one end
that the life-processes leading to cleavage cannot penetrate

through it, and as a result only the animal part segments, forming a cap of cells resting on undivided yolk. This is of particular interest, since this partial or as it is called *meroblastic* cleavage is characteristic of many animals, such as fish, reptiles, and birds. Experiment thus makes it evident that the character of partial cleavage in these forms is not the result of any special evolutionary adaptations, but a direct and necessary consequence of the accumulation of a great store of yolk within the egg-cell.

A still further deduction of the same kind can be made. In birds and sharks, a number of nuclei of the border-line cells migrate out into the yolk, and there take on a characteristic appearance.

In the artificially meroblastic frog's egg, nuclei of this same type appear in the undivided portion—again making it probable that the peculiar appearance of these yolk-nuclei, and indeed their migration itself, are the inevitable results of this particular distribution of materials.

As a result of the operations of Balfour's and Hertwig's rules, not only are the vegetative cells larger than their animal brothers, but they have divided less frequently. It is probable that all the processes of life are slowed down by the yolk, so that it is reasonable to conclude that the vegetative cells are less advanced than the animal cells, in that they have not travelled so far along the path leading to differentiation. There would thus by the close of segmentation be an animal-vegetative or axial gradient, not only in cell-size and yolk-content, but also in degree of differentiation.

Another series of experiments has been devoted to the problem of discovering whether the symmetry of the egg and its segmentation had any relation to the symmetry of the later embryo. It was taken for granted to start with that the animal pole gave rise to the back of the tadpole, but later observation made it clear that this was not so. The egg is free to adjust its position within the jelly membrane owing to the presence of a layer of fluid which appears there immediately upon fertilisation, and, to cut a long story short, it was eventually shown that towards the close of gastrulation the egg tilts round as a result of internal re-arrangement of the heavy yolk, just as an iceberg rolls over in the sea when it grows top-heavy. As a result of this the blastopore comes to lie on the equator at the hind end, with the original animal pole pointing slightly downwards, a little below the future front end of the head. Thus the position of what we may call the 'virtual embryo' in the egg is such that the animal pole is roughly in the position of the future mouth, the vegetative pole in the position of the future tail.

But what about the first furrow of segmentation? It would seem most natural to suppose that this divided the material for the future right and left halves of the embryo, and this assumption was very generally made. However, it was eventually proved that, although this relation did quite often hold, yet it was very far from being a necessary one, and that indeed the first furrow might make any angle whatever with the future median plane. This holds not only for the frog, but for the newt: but in both animals, in the great majority of cases, it runs so as *either* to divide future right and left halves, *or* to separate dorsal from ventral.

In the frog, however, the fertilised egg shows a character not present before fertilisation—the so-called grey crescent, a patch on one side where some of the black pigment has been drawn into the interior; and this is found to coincide, in the great majority of cases, with the future plane of symmetry. The grey crescent forms an hour or two after fertilisation, and we now know it to be caused by the sperm. It is formed on the diametrically opposite meridian to that on which the sperm has entered. Thus one of the most fundamental attributes of the future frog is not predetermined in the egg at all, but is fixed by the accident of the sperm's point of entry. Perhaps it would be fairer to say that what is predetermined in the egg is the possibility of becoming bilaterally symmetrical about an infinity of axes; and that the sperm entry-point chooses which one of these axes it shall be. In one of the sea-weeds, Lund has recently shown that the future axis may be determined by something even more extraneous, namely the direction of a weak electric current passed through the water in which the fertilised ova are lying.

The experiment already mentioned, of compressing the segmenting egg between glass plates, serves yet another purpose. By this means the order of the cleavages is altered, and so nuclei distributed to cells and regions of the body other than those to which they would normally be assigned: and yet, if the egg be released at the close of segmentation, a normal embryo results. The only conclusion to be drawn from this is that the nuclei are all equivalent as regards their effect on differentiation. No division of the original single nucleus of the egg into qualitatively unlike nuclei, as supposed by Roux, can occur.

Another experiment that helped to demonstrate the physiological equivalence of the nuclei was the separation of the two first blastomeres, which resulted in the production of twin larvae, normal in every detail of form. This was demonstrated for the newt (Fig. 12). Partial constriction

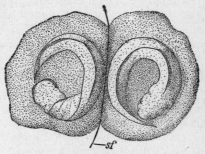

FIG. 12.—Twin half-sized newt embryo, produced by separating the first two cells by constriction with a fine hair (*sf*)

produces partial doubling of 'Siamese twins' (Fig. 13). The separation is very difficult to effect in the frog, owing to the consistency of the materials of the egg; but if one blastomere is killed with a hot needle and then carefully cleaned away, an approximation is obtained to the clean-cut result in the newt.

This introduces us to a new property of the living material of the egg, which we may call that of regulation. The portion of substance which in its normal position would have developed into a half, has the power, if isolated, of regulating itself and its internal structure so as to give rise to a whole. This regulation is, in the newt, apparent from the first. The isolated blastomeres round off, and form almost normal spherical blastulae and gastrulae. In some other animals, a curious and interesting difference is apparent. The '½-blastomere' (as an isolated one of the first 2 blastomeres is styled for brevity's sake) segments as a half, almost exactly as if it were still in contact with its mate, but on reaching the close of segmentation it rounds up into a normal-shaped though of course miniature blastula. This is so in the sea-urchin. Thus in these cases what we may call the pattern of segmentation has no influence upon the future course of differentiation—a conclusion also forced upon us by the results of the pressure-experiments in which irregular plates of cells are produced, and yet can and do give rise to normal animals.

When we find that the segmenting egg may thus be divided into two and yet each half form a whole, we are tempted

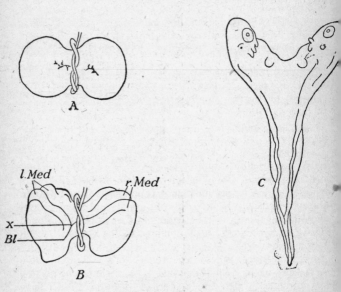

FIG. 13.—(A) A newt gastrula partially constricted by means of a hair. Note the two parts of the blastopore on either side of the hair. (B) Later stage. Two sets of neural folds are developing, separate in front (*l.* Med and *r.* Med), united behind (at X). (C) The final result—a monster with two anterior ends.

to say that not only are the nuclei all equivalent but also that the first furrow may divide the cytoplasm in any way without affecting the result—in other words, that the future symmetry of the embryo is not influenced by anything that

one could call a ' determiner ' in the cytoplasm.[1] Again,
however, first impressions would not be right. Although
in newts separation of the first two blastomeres *may* produce
two equivalent and similar twins, in a large percentage nothing
of the sort occurs, but only one of the two isolated blastomeres
gives a normal embryo, while the other, although it segments
normally and produces germ-layers, never proceeds beyond
this stage of differentiation, but dies without showing a trace
of nervous system, notochord, or muscle-segments. The
clue to this fact was given by another experiment. Spemann
had previously found that twin larvae might not only be
produced from the first two blastomeres, but also when the
division was made during segmentation, or at its close,
or after gastrulation had just begun. No visible grey crescent
appears in the newt's egg, so that until the blastopore arises
it is not possible to tell the relation of the first furrow to the
symmetry of the embryo. But if the hair with which the germ
is later to be cut in two is tied along the first furrow so as to
produce a slight constriction, and the egg then allowed to
proceed to gastrulation, then immediately the first portion,
or dorsal lip, of the blastopore appears we know how our
constriction is related to the future embryo.

By using this method, Spemann found that when the
first furrow was median, and consequently passed right
through the dorsal lip, then division produced two equivalent
larvae: but when it was frontal, separating future dorsal
and ventral halves, then the dorsal lip of the blastopore lay
entirely in one of the two portions: this portion produced
a normal embryo, the other only gave rise to an undifferentiated sphere.

By cutting the late blastula or early gastrula in various
directions, Spemann was then able to show that the something which made this difference between success and failure
in development was a quite small piece of the germ situated
near the equator on one side of the egg after fertilisation.
Just below this region the dorsal lip forms during gastrulation,

[1] The first furrow always runs from animal to vegetative pole:
thus both of the first two blastomeres always contain the whole
gamut of strata—the whole axial gradient. If it were to run parallel
to the equator and separate the less and more yolky halves of the
egg, such qualitative division would certainly be followed by
qualitative differences in the resulting embryos.

and in front of the dorsal lip, and only there, does the first differentiation of tissues take place.

We shall see later that Spemann himself has been able to establish in the most brilliant way the direct connection between dorsal lip and differentiation—what we may call the organising capacity of this region. Meanwhile he had already demonstrated, by the fact that the percentage of ½-blastomeres which failed to develop was the same as that of the half-gastrulae which lacked part of the dorsal lip and were also unable to develop, not only that the presence of a dorsal lip region was necessary for further development, but also that this determiner of development could be traced right back to the fertilised egg before segmentation had begun, and that the visible appearance of the dorsal lip was only one in a chain of processes which had been set agoing long before.

Quite recently, Mangold has performed some beautiful and ingenious experiments which bear out this view. It had been known for some time that not only was it possible to produce twins by separating the first two blastomeres of an egg, but that the converse result was also possible—of uniting two separate eggs to give a single over-sized larva. This had only been performed on invertebrates, and was regarded as another proof of the equivalence of the cytoplasm round the axis of the egg.

With the newt's egg, Spemann had found how to remove it from its protecting membrane—a necessary preliminary to many delicate pieces of research. When thus freed, however, it is no longer properly supported, and flattens out into a cake-like form: and when it divides for the first time, the two ½-blastomeres pull a good way apart during division, so that a dumb-bell shape is produced. As division comes to an end, they pull together again. Mangold took advantage of this temporary dumb-bell phase: and, by catching up one dividing egg in a double ' belt ' made of two hair-loops fastened on to a fine glass tube, was able to lift it and place it crossways over another egg in the same stage.

As the first division came to an end, the four blastomeres were pulled together and came into contact, and from then till the close of segmentation no difference could be detected between the behaviour of this curiously compounded double monster and a normal egg. Still more remarkable, Mangold was able in this way to join eggs of different species of newts —the light-coloured eggs of one species with the dark ones of another. None the less, the blastomeres of the two animal kinds joined up with each other just as readily as those of the same kind, and the blastula was a chimaera or mosaic of two organisms, in which the contributions of the two partners could be immediately distinguished, although the two kinds of cells fitted together as snugly as could be wished. Now the first furrow might have divided either of the two eggs in either of the two ways, along the future plane of symmetry, or else to separate dorsal from ventral. It will be clear that various possibilities could thus be realised. If the division and subsequent rearrangement happened to be in one way, the two should grow to a single embryo; another way, and a double or treble monster should be the result. All the different possible combinations to be deduced theoretically were actually realised.

Another variation of the same experiment is to separate the first two blastomeres of a single egg and then, when each of them assumes the dumb-bell form during its division, to place them across each other so that the blastomeres that should have neighboured each other now come alternately. Again there are various theoretical possibilities of development into a double or a single creature: and again Mangold found all the possibilities realised.

It appears then quite definite that immediately after fertilisation an area is to be found in the egg which determines the whole future symmetry of the resulting animal. Not only this, but, as we shall see later, this same area also determines the actual differentiation of organs, so as to deserve the title of ' organiser ' which Spemann bestows upon it.

Spemann and his pupils have also in the last few years traced back another determining factor to the very earliest stages—the factor which determines the asymmetry of the future animal. As is well known, vertebrates in general are asymmetrical, the heart being a little to the left side, the stomach and liver correspondingly bent. It is also well known that in a small percentage of cases, among men as well as other organisms, the normal position is reversed— a condition technically known as *situs inversus viscerum ;* such individuals are like mirror-reflections of the normal type. What is less generally known, however, is that in man a large proportion of individuals with this reversed symmetry are members of pairs of identical twins—*i.e.* organisms which have been derived from half only of the material derived from a fertilised egg.

When twinning is incomplete, double monsters are the result, which may be of all grades, from the almost-freedom of the famous Siamese twins down to a condition when only the heads or part of the heads are double. When such double monsters are examined, it is found not only that they too yield a high proportion of symmetry-reversals, but that the reversed organism or part-organism is almost invariably the right-hand member of the pair.

So much for observation: now for experiment. Spemann, some years back, had been able to demonstrate that a lighter degree of constriction than that needed to divide the newt germ into two separate parts would, if it were along the future median plane, produce double monsters. The duplicity of these was at the anterior end, and by varying the strength of constriction, all grades of it could be produced at will, from a third eye between duplicated fore-brains down to creatures double for half their length. This partial doubling, like complete separation, could be produced at any stage from the first cleavage to the onset of gastrulation.

When the doubling extends as far as the heart and stomach, it is found that here too, when inverse *situs* occurs, it is almost exclusively in the right partial twin: and the same is true of the right-hand member of pairs of separate twins.

Two further facts are of interest in this connection. In the first place, the inner side, even of completely separate newt twins, is frequently and indeed usually less well developed than the outer, the gills and limbs being smaller or even wanting, and the body more or less bent in. In the second place, it was found that if a small portion of the embryo just after gastrulation were cut out, in the region a little in front of the blastopore, and on the left side, then the resulting larvae were indifferent as to their symmetry, right- and left-handedness occurring in roughly equal proportions. This indicates that, in the late embryo at least, a particular small area is concerned with securing the normal dominance of left-handed symmetry, its removal leaving the result a prey to chance: while, on the other hand, the fact that right-handed symmetry develops in an abnormally large percentage of larvae from right-hand blastomeres after separation at the first cleavage, indicates that some determiner is already present even then. Spemann is inclined to think that the answer to the riddle must be sought in the ultimate molecular structure of the egg, many compounds, as is well known, being capable of existing in two forms which differ only in the right- or left-handed symmetry of their component molecules.

In this connection it is of interest to remember that the pattern of segmentation in many eggs is asymmetrical, and that in the snails and their allies the type of segmentation, whether right- or left-handed, determines the future asymmetry of the whole body, the rare individuals with left-wound shells being derived from left-handedly segmenting eggs. And hereditary studies seem to indicate that the cause of this asymmetry is to be sought in the processes leading to the formation of the egg in the parent's ovary.

Spemann is inclined to think that the left-hand side is in some way normally ' stronger ' than the right, and that this determines the normal ascendancy of left-handedness: this view is supported by the experiments of Warynski and Fol, who, by slightly damaging the left side of an early chick embryo by heat, were able to induce a reversal of symmetry in the whole. Finally, it is interesting to notice that when the asymmetry is exaggerated in any respect, it may in some sense pervade the body and induce secondary changes. For instance, in female birds the right ovary disappears during embryonic growth: the left side must therefore be more ' dominant ' than usual: and it is found when investigating the inheritance of the extra toe found in some breeds that it occurs more often and better developed on the left than on the right foot.

Finally, it remains to mention one or two other experiments bearing upon these early stages. We know that there is a stratification of yolk and another of glycogen within the unfertilised egg, and, of course, within the germ at the close of segmentation. Do these substances have a formative effect upon future development? and if so, is this effect specific, or of a more general nature?

The answer to these questions is largely given by experiments of Jenkinson, who analysed the effects produced by centrifuging frogs' eggs at different speeds, after fertilisation but before segmentation. The immediate effect of the treatment was of course a more or less complete separation of the different constituents of the egg according to the specific gravity. The heavy yolk was concentrated more than ever at one pole, the fat at the opposite pole. The living cytoplasm constituted an intermediate layer, which we may reasonably suppose to have been itself in some degree stratified, and a good deal of the heavy pigment on the animal hemisphere was driven down on to the surface of and even into the mass of yolk. If the centrifuging was light, development was normal, save for the fact that the organs in the head region contained an abnormal quantity of fat, often in numerous and quite large globules. If it was heavy, development ceased at or before gastrulation. With intermediate treatment, various degrees of abnormality resulted. The essential points about all such cases except the most severe was that the head region was degenerate while the trunk region was more or less normal, and that the yolk-mass in the intestine was often solid and undivided, a condition which itself was further often the cause of incomplete closure of the blastopore. These two facts are to be readily accounted for. The undivided and inert condition of the yolk is due to the separation of a layer of yolk at the centrifugal pole from which practically all cytoplasm has been forced out; and the degeneration of the head-region is due to the presence in the animal pole, near which the head arises, of fat in such great proportion as to prevent development—an artificial fatty degeneration.

But it is of much interest to find that yolk and fat are not organ-forming substances in the strict sense—a definite amount of each is by no means necessary for the development of any special organ; on the contrary, differentiation appears to pursue its course, independent within very wide limits of the materials in which it occurs, provided solely that a certain minimum percentage of living protoplasm is present. The normal form of the parts of the brain are almost perfectly preserved even though the percentage of fat is multiplied perhaps tenfold within its cells; and the same is true for the differentiation of the front of the trunk even though the major portion of its yolk has been forced down towards the future hind-limb region.

The yolk certainly and obviously exerts a differentiating effect in that its stratification determines a gradient in cell-size and cell-activity at the close of segmentation, and this in its turn determines that the smaller cells shall give epidermis and nervous system, the larger cells shall turn into a particular part of the gut. But this is a roundabout way, and a very different thing from asserting that yolk or even heavy yolk-content is a *specific* pre-requisite for gut-differentiation. As a matter of fact it is clearly not, since a great deal of the gut is produced from cells folded in at the lip of the blastopore, and containing relatively little yolk. So in building a house we might put more bricks into the top storey, more concrete into the basement. But these are still *raw* materials, and we could ' differentiate ' a basement out of brick just as well: the specificity of basement as against attics depends on other and subtler causes.

In the frog, then, and in other amphibia, the processes of differentiation simply utilise the available raw materials, of whose nature they are relatively independent. But just as it would be impossible for human builders to add the top storey to a house if they had exhausted all but a minute stock of bricks and iron, and were left with nothing but glass, so there are limits to the type and proportions of the materials which the self-building organism can utilise for its own construction.

In this respect, however, the frog's method, although it is probably typical, is certainly not the only one. Animals do exist in which during segmentation certain materials preformed in the unfertilised egg are distributed to special regions of the embryo, where they are necessary as constituents of special organs. This is the case in Dentalium, the tusk-shell, and in several other invertebrates. If we continued our building simile, we might compare such an animal to a house of which a conservatory was an integral part, and say that the major part of the available glass was transported to its site before building began. But these similes from human affairs are rarely complete. We must not forget that the developing animal not only utilises such

special materials, but generates them during the progress
of development from the raw stuffs of its food or the reserves
accumulated within it. It appears highly probable that cases
such as that of Dentalium really mean not only that there
is a precocious *segregation* of material, but a precocious
formation of special material from raw material, followed
by its segregation into the proper areas. Such materials
as are present in the frog's egg are much more probably
in the nature of raw material only, the special materials not
being produced till the start of primary differentiation, *i.e.*
during late gastrulation. It is interesting to note, as Wilson,
Boveri, and others have pointed out, that there exists every
gradation from eggs in which there is precocious formation
and distribution of specific organ-forming substances, and
those more primitive types in which only raw materials are
present, and the only arrangement is a simple and graded
stratification.

The close of gastrulation is the beginning of a new epoch—
an epoch of rapid and widespread differentiation of visible
structure. Recent work has shed a new light upon many
of the processes involved, so that it will be better to throw
the historical method by the board and use the new to
illuminate the old.

Earlier experiments had shown that the something which
determined the formation of a dorsal lip was also connected
in some way with subsequent differentiation, since if the germ
was divided so as to confine the dorsal lip region, or its
precursor, to one half, the other half never proceeded further
than the formation of germ-layers. It then became an obvious
task to discover more precisely where this structure-determiner
was situated and how it acted. This was eventually achieved
by the beautiful method of embryonic grafting elaborated
by Spemann. A tiny portion of one embryo is sucked up
into a micropipette and its connections then severed by means
of an exceedingly fine glass filament. A similar operation
is performed on another embryo, and the two pieces can then
be interchanged. If light pressure is applied for a short time,
the wounds heal perfectly. It was first found that different
eggs of one and the same species of newt might differ considerably in colour; accordingly grafts from a light to a dark
egg, or *vice versâ*, could for a long time be distinguished.

Becoming more ambitious, Spemann then tried grafting pieces from the egg of one species on to another, and again got perfect healing. This enabled him to trace the fate of the implanted bits for a much longer period, since the histological characters of the tissues differ from one species to the other.

The ectoderm of the region between the dorsal lip's final position and the animal pole will normally give rise to the medullary plate, which in its turn is the pre-determined precursor of the whole nervous system: we may call this ectoderm the virtual medullary plate. Almost all the remainder of the ectoderm will give rise to simple epidermis. By interchanging bits of the actual or the virtual medullary plate at different times with epidermis from different places, a number of interesting points were established.

If the interchange is made at the beginning of gastrulation, then it is without effect on the future course of events: the piece that ought to have made a part of the brain or spinal cord settles down to the more humdrum task of making part of the outer layer of the skin, and *vice versâ*.

This was so even when the piece came from another species. Differentiation knows no specific boundaries, it appears, and the engrafted piece is modelled to form whatever is expected of it in its station in life—be it skin, inner ear, a portion of brain, or what not.

But if it is made at the close of gastrulation, this is no longer possible. The virtual epidermis, although still not visibly differentiated as such, yet has suffered some invisible differentiation, for it now refuses to form medullary plate tissue when grafted into medullary plate region.

The same is true of the reverse operation, which, however, is in some ways even more interesting. When, at this later stage, virtual medullary plate is grafted into the epidermis of flank or belly, it shows that it too has received the secret impulse. Its cells become elongated: the piece sinks down and at the same time its edges roll inwards, in much the same way as the untouched normal medullary plate is sunk below the surface and rolled in to form the nerve-tube; the transplanted fragment thus does its best to achieve its normal development.

We may justly say that by this time the destinies of all

the various regions of the germ are now predetermined, though not visibly differentiated.

Thus between these two moments—separated in time by only a few hours—something has happened which has started the various regions irreversibly on their proper paths of development. But the mechanism of it all still remained obscure. Finally, however, Spemann discovered that if a quite small piece of the region just above the dorsal lip were grafted into the virtual epidermis of the future flank of another embryo, then a medullary plate would be formed in this region—as well, of course, as the normal medullary plate formed in connection with the host's own dorsal lip. The prettiest demonstration came when, after grafting the dorsal lip region of one species into the darker flank tissues of another, he saw the dark host tissues differentiating into medullary plate round the lighter graft: differentiation is thus *induced* in the regions near the graft, not brought about by increase of the engrafted tissue. The dorsal lip region therefore is not a region predetermined to form medullary plate, but predetermined to make other regions form medullary plate. Spemann calls it an ' organisator ': *organising centre* or *differentiator* will perhaps serve our purpose in English—something from which there spreads an influence, hitherto unanalysed, maybe physical or maybe chemical, which calls out latent possibilities in other tissues. It is like Mother Carey in Kingsley's *Water Babies*, who ' made things make themselves.'

The one solid fact that we know about this region is that it is at this time the region of most active growth in the organism.

This, however, is a very real start; for at one sweep it gives us solid ground to go on in the marsh of speculation. Differentiation here (and we shall see that the differentiator has not only been responsible for the appearance of medullary plate but of the first of a whole series of reactions, which inevitably follow once the train is fired, and lead to the differentiation of the whole organism)—differentiation here is not due to the qualitative distribution of nuclear factors: not simply to the distribution of different ' organ-forming substances ' to different regions of the germ: but to an impetus given by one region to other regions.

An interesting parallel to this behaviour was found by Child some time ago in the regeneration of planarian worms. These little flat leaf-like creatures possess a head with primitive brain, touch-organs and eye-spots, while their mouth is in the centre of the under side, on the end of a muscular pharynx which can be protruded like a proboscis or trunk.

As is well known, these animals have an almost unlimited power of regeneration. It is a simple affair to them to grow a new head or tail if they are cut in two, since they may be even chopped into a score of fragments, and any of these may reorganise itself into a whole, so that it is easy enough to make two planarians grow where one grew before. But even so, proper regeneration does not always occur. When conditions are not altogether favourable, a new head will not form on the posterior piece after the animal has been cut across. If the cut is made just behind the pharynx, Child was able to establish as an absolute rule that the regeneration of a new pharynx was dependent upon the previous regeneration of a new head. If a head appears, a pharynx appears; but if no head, then no pharynx. On the other hand, pieces from in front of the pharynx might sometimes grow a new pharynx even in the absence of a head. In other words, the presence of some region which is normally in front of the pharynx is necessary for the formation of a pharynx. The regenerated pharynx is in any case not formed out of the bud of new tissue at the anterior cut surface. It is laid down among the old tissues, reorganised from out of them. Other organs behave in the same way: but the pharynx is visible to casual inspection, and is therefore best taken as an example. The head thus exerts an influence upon the differentiation of the rest of the body which is very similar to that exerted by the newt's primary differentiator: in both cases one region initiates differentiation in other regions. There is a difference: for while in the worm it is an already differentiated region which acts as organising centre, in the newt the centre possesses no visible differentiation whatever.

There is, however, a further and equally fundamental resemblance. It is in the possession of a system of physiological gradients in worms and eggs alike.

The subject is so important that a brief digression upon

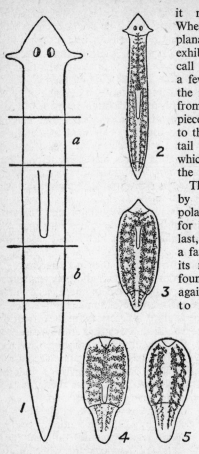

it may be pardoned. When small pieces of a planarian regenerate, they exhibit what we may call polarity; for (with a few special exceptions) the new head is formed from that region of the piece which was nearest to the old head, the new tail from that region which was nearest to the old tail.

This polarity, so called by analogy with the polarity of a magnet, was for long mysterious. At last, however, we are in a fair way to understand its nature. It has been found possible (and this again we owe to Child) to substitute a new polarity for the old. Any one who has been through a course in biology will remember the hydroid polyps — primitive but beautiful creatures with a mouth in the midst of a circlet of tentacles, and a ' body ' consisting of a two-layered tube surrounding a space which combines the functions of digestion and circulation.

Fig. 14.—Regeneration in Planaria.
(1) Outline of adult, indicating at *a* and *b* the regions cut out; (2) Complete regeneration of (*a*) or (*b*) when new head is formed; (3) Rudimentary head formed in adverse conditions: pharynx produced both in (*a*) and (*b*); (4) Headless (*a*)-piece; a pharynx is formed; (5) Headless (*b*)-piece; no pharynx formed.

If a portion of this body-region is cut out, it will regenerate, and the new mouth and tentacles will be produced at the end nearest the old mouth. In one hydroid, known as Corymorpha, if such a piece of stem be placed in water to which weak poisons or narcotics are added, it will undergo the same sort of changes that we saw take place in Clavellina in similar circumstances—it will become simpler, lose its differentiation, and finally be converted into a sausage-shaped semi-opaque mass of tissue, adhering to the bottom of the vessel. If clean sea-water is now substituted for the narcotic solution, regeneration will take place in a few days, and a complete polyp be formed; the mouth, however, appears not at one end of the piece, but at the top, where the tissues are farthest removed from the glass, and most exposed to oxygen. (Fig. 15).

From this and a number of other experiments on many animal forms, Child has framed a wide-reaching generalisation styled by him the theory of axial gradients, or perhaps better, physiological gradients.

The establishment of some sort of main gradient from apex to base in the undifferentiated egg or bud is the first essential step in the process. Many eggs, for instance, are so attached in the parent's ovary that one side is fixed, the other free and exposed directly to the nutritive fluids. Thus one pole is supplied with more oxygen than the other, and so a gradient in degree of activity will be established, the processes of life working more quickly at one end than at the other. The exact nature of the ' activity ' in which one end of the gradient differs from the other is still in doubt. Experiments by Lund indicate that under one aspect at least it is probably electrical.

Furthermore, it is found that the structures and organs which exist at the more active end of the gradient are relatively independent, and in some degree dominate the rest.

In the planarian worm, for example, if regeneration takes place at all at an anterior cut surface, a head is formed. The head, the most active region, is that which is independently or first generated by the plastic tissues of the creature. Once it has arisen, however, it takes command, and remodels the structure of the piece from which it has originated so that eventually a perfect whole is produced from what at one time consists of a head stuck disproportionately on to a random segment of the body. The same is true for many other animals; and we are thus justified in saying that the head or apical region is not only itself relatively independent, but dominates in some as yet unexplained way the remainder of the body.

From studies on low animals and early stages, then, we come away with various fundamental ideas. We have first the general idea of gradients, and then the conception

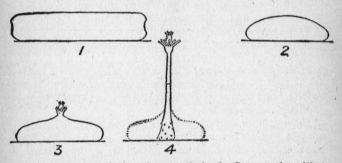

FIG. 15.—Establishment of new polarity in Corymorpha. (1) A piece of stem; normally this should produce a polyp towards the right (the original polyp end). (2) The piece of stem dedifferentiated in alcohol. (3), (4) Regeneration with new polarity on replacement in sea-water.

that an organism can be thought of as a system in which, as in society, one part is dominant over the rest. Let us now jump to the higher forms, and see whether these ideas help us.

The higher animals, such as birds or mammals, differ from those we have been considering in two chief ways. They possess an enormously better-developed brain; and they are much more independent of their environment, much more self-regulating. To deal only with the second point, they have the power of regulating the temperature of the body, come cold, come heat, within a fraction of a degree. The chemical constitution of the blood is kept constant with an almost alarming accuracy; for instance an increase of one part of the acidity-producing hydrogen ion in one hundred million parts of blood will cause an increase in the rate of breathing which, by washing carbonic acid out through the lungs, will restore the normal acidity. Not least, the rates of growth and of differentiation, the rate of working of the whole machine, the quality of much of the psychic side of life, are determined by the secretions of the ductless glands, such as the thyroid or pituitary, which amounts are again most carefully regulated

Meanwhile, with the rise of mind in evolution, changes have taken place in the nature of dominance. The brain is in contact with all other parts of the body by means of nerves; it becomes more and more complex; it receives more news of the outer world through improved sense-organs, and can deal better with that information as it develops mechanisms for memory or reason. It becomes the dominant part of the organism. In man, that part of the brain associated with mind is dominant over the rest; so that if we like we may say, *tout court*, that mind dominates the human organism.

It has been said before—' Ideas rule the world ' is an old proverb—but it is none the less important to have it formulated in a more general way. A healthy body is so much machinery: what use shall be made of it depends on the mind which dominates its working. To what extent this dominance may run is seen in everyday life in those who have some fixed belief or overruling passion.

The miser's thoughts and actions are devoted to the amassing and hoarding of wealth, the lover's to the object of his love; those of the neurasthenic who persists in believing that he is incapable of any achievement are paralysed and brought to nothing. But even within the mind itself, the same relation of dominance and subordination is at work; only here matters are more complex, owing to the plasticity of mind, and to the fact that in psycho-neural processes of this kind the permanent and the structural are subordinated to the functional and temporary.

It is impossible here to go into any detail of psychology; but one may perhaps be permitted to indicate one or two lines along which the concept is of value. In the first place, dominance without something to dominate is useless. Under certain circumstances, one can so cut a flat-worm that nothing but a head shall result from the piece; such structures are biological superfluities, doomed to speedy death. Now recent work on psychology has shown that by a process of repression the higher centres of the human mind are capable of pushing anything unpleasant out of connection with themselves, into a sort of mental limbo. Usually it is the thoughts connected with whole instincts, such as the sexual instinct or the instinct of fear, which are thus repressed. However, though repressed, they have their revenge; they continually attempt to reach the surface of consciousness again, and so ensues a conflict between two parts of the mind, a conflict which leads eventually to neurasthenia, depression, breakdown, or hysteria. In other men—perhaps the majority—complete repression is not attempted, conflict never arises, and the two tendencies, that of the simple instinct and that of the higher rational centres, exist side by side. Finally, however, there are those rare spirits to whom conflict comes but is an opportunity for a new conciliation. They face the instinct which seems to threaten the higher things of the mind, and put it in subordination to them. They do not repress, but the fact that their higher centres are dominant only allows the subordinate system to develop to a certain degree and in a certain way. Finally, by the fact of association between different parts of the mind, it is possible for the higher centres to receive strength from their subordinates, and the lower instincts to be what psychologists call sublimated, and so their driving force turned into new and worthier channels. Pure repression aims at producing a ruler without a kingdom. The properly sublimated mind alone has the true organic unity.

But we must recall our straying footsteps from human mind to amphibian gastrulation. For our present purpose the especially important points are these. First, in the frog's egg at the onset of gastrulation there exist two main gradients —the apico-basal from animal to vegetative pole, manifested most clearly in the proportion of yolk in the cells, and the dorso-ventral, from dorsal lip to future ventral surface, manifested in the rapidity of cell-division in the region of the equator. From other forms we know that, in general, the most active region is the dominant one; and, in particular, a certain level of activity must be reached in regenerating tissue at an anterior cut surface if a head is to arise there. Now the dorsal lip region of the amphibian blastopore is also the most active region of the germ. Its cells are multiplying more rapidly than any others, as is revealed in the much greater activity of growth in this region.

Although the detailed mechanism at present escapes us, we are, I think, justified in concluding that in both these cases, and probably in many others, the impulse to differentiation comes from a region of high activity and acts upon regions of lower intensity. We come back, that is, to the notion of a gradient. This is of some importance, for it serves to make less puzzling a fact which I must confess has often perplexed me, although from the absence of reference to the problem in the literature of the subject, it does not seem to have perplexed others. It is this: if, as seems clear, Child's theory of physiological gradients contains a seed of essential truth, if, that is, the rate of activity has an influence upon differentiation, how comes it that the absolute rate of activity can be altered within wide limits, as by different temperatures, and yet development be identical or almost so at every level? The answer, it seems, is that the start of differentiation is, within wide limits, not concerned with absolute values of activity, but with the *relation* between the different activities of two regions—in other words, with what we may fairly call a difference in potential of some sort or other. And such a conclusion is clearly of considerable theoretical importance.

This period, once initiated by the activity of the differentiator, which we may call the period of primary differentiation, has some very interesting characteristics. It is extremely rapid as well as multifarious in results: it is apparently a complex of irreversible processes which, once initiated, run on inevitably to their appointed end even if the regions in which they occur are separated from each other. From all appearances, it looks as if a whole series of well-marked chemical reactions had been set going, most of which are quite independent of the rest. The organism at the close of this stage is predominantly what with justice may be called a chemical mosaic. This mosaic differentiation can be shown in a number of ways. If, for instance, the front end of the early medullary plate be cut out and grafted back again in reversed orientation, it will differentiate into precisely the same parts as it would have if it had been left in place, with the result of course that they are now in reversed order with reference to the rest of the organism. A small piece of the edges of the medullary plate near the front end will proceed to give rise to an eye below the epidermis just as it would have *in situ*. Spemann has even been able to show conclusively that the three visibly different portions of the embryonic eye—the optic stalk, the pigment or tapetal layer, and the retina, are all predetermined in the medullary plate before it has begun to sink in to form a tube, and long before the first rudiment of the future eye is visible as such.

Nasal organ, auditory organ, heart, limbs, gills—all these have also been shown to be predetermined some time before they show any visible differentiation: and it is at least probable that all the other separate organs of the body are differentiated in the same way.

It seems inevitable to suppose that these qualitative differences between organs are due to qualitative chemical differences; and I therefore propose the term *chemo-differentiation* for this phase of development. It is interesting to notice that while the quality and type of the organ is thus chemically determined, its precise form often appears due to physical causes. For instance, when a piece of medullary plate is reversed, it may happen that the cut has divided the eye-region into two. Owing to the way the substances for the retinal and tapetal layers lie in the plate, such a cut will leave the front half of the eye with too little, the back half with too much tapetal substance—a disproportion whose effects are visible for a considerable time. But as regards form, there is no such segregation. Each of the two portions, provided it has *some* of both the two sorts of material, will form an optic cup in the regular way, or with a good approach to the regular way: it will never form a half-cup. This would be accounted for if the form-generating processes at work were due to some mechanical or physical property of the eye-rudiment, of the nature perhaps of surface-tension, or growth-difference between the two components, and not to chemical differences.

This machine-like separate differentiation of parts is

also seen if the late gastrula or the neurula is bisected as a whole: each part, although it rounds itself off owing to physical causes, produces just those organs which it would have produced as part of the whole, and no more—an independence in striking contrast to the regulation previously displayed by the earlier stages. If the front half of one species be grafted on to the back half of another species, both

continue to differentiate, and a chimaera or mosaic organism is produced. Harrison succeeded in rearing such compound tadpoles right through metamorphosis! This

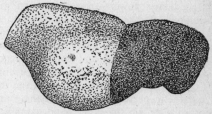

FIG. 16a.—Anterior half of *Rana sylvatica* grafted on to posterior half of *R. palustris*. (*Re-drawn after Harrison*)

passage from a regulating to a non-regulating condition takes place during gastrulation, before the first structural differentiation, in the shape of the medullary plate, is visible at all.

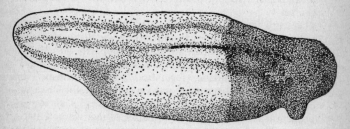

FIG. 16b.—The same, later stage. The lateral line of *R. sylvatica* (pigmented) is growing on to the tissues of *R. palustris* (unpigmented). (*Re-drawn after Harrison*)

Spemann found that, when the top half of the gastrula was cut off as soon as the dorsal lip had appeared, regulation still occurred in it, and the medullary plate and all other subsequent organs were of half-size, proportionate to the half-sized embryonic fragment. But if the constriction was delayed until the blastopore had become circular, no regulation was possible, the medullary plate was of full size, and therefore so much out of proportion with the half-fragment that it was unable to close to a tube.

What is in some ways more curious still is the fact that this period of non-regulation not only succeeds one regulatory phase, but precedes another. Once the tissues of the organism have become differentiated and it is capable of function, extraordinary powers of regeneration and regulation are developed. If the whole of the limb-bud region is excised at or just before its first appearance, no limb is ever formed: but even in an adult newt the whole hind-limb and pelvic girdle can be excised and complete regeneration will yet occur. A section of spinal cord in the limb region can even be cut out without interfering with the result, provided the sympathetic nerve-chain is not damaged. In the chemical mosaic stage, on the other hand, complete limb-failure can be produced by cutting out a little block of mesoderm in the future limb-area. Limb-failure can be produced even when a limb-girdle is subsequently differentiated. In the same way, the tail of any amphibian tadpole will regenerate if cut across: but cutting off the tip of the tail-bud in early stages will, as Schaxel found, produce a permanently short-tailed organism.

These are facts of great importance for their bearing on theoretical biology. Driesch and the neo-vitalists, Haldane and the organicists, both lay stress on the capacity for regulation as a specific possession of life, and as its most distinctive character. For Haldane, regulation places organisms in a different category from any non-living systems: for Driesch, it demands the intervention of vitalistic ' forces ' such as his hypothetical entelechy. But as a matter of fact we now find that certainly in amphibia, with every degree of probability in all other vertebrates, and very likely in many or all invertebrates too, that what is by far the most important single phase in development—the laying down of the distinctive architecture of the body and the complete basis of its future function—is a process in which regulation is reduced to a minimum and, as regards qualitative chemical differentiation, is conspicuously absent. In other words, chemo-differentiation, while it may and indeed certainly does involve biochemical processes of extraordinary complexity, is, so far as we have any means of judging at present, a subject for the biochemist and not a problem *sui generis*.

It remains for us to ask if there is any clue to the course of events while this primary differentiation is being determined. Here again a number of important points have been elicited. Spemann found that if moderate median constriction is applied to the egg, then various intermediate steps towards twinning result, the embryo being partially double (see Fig. 13). The doubling always involves the anterior end, and usually the anterior end only; and the degree to which doubling runs down the body depends upon the tightness of the constriction. This is really another proof that the differentiator acts upon neutral tissue, not predetermined in any fixed way, and that the chemo-differentiation of an organ, such as for instance the eye, is determined by its relation to some path along which the impulse to differentiation is spreading. If this is so, and the constriction splits the path of differentiation and diverts it to either side, then the observed results will follow.

But there are certain other facts which at first sight are very hard to reconcile with the ideas I have been putting forward. As a result of various causes, but usually of some unfavourable condition of chemical environment, embryos are produced with cyclopian defect—in other words, with but one eye, and that median, like the mythical cyclops (Fig. 17). When this is the case, the median eye generally shows traces of being derived from two rudiments, and the parts which normally lie between the two eyes are missing, as if a wedge had been simply dug out of the front end of the embryo after differentiation had started. The origin of this condition has been investigated with special care by Stockard in fish. By placing the fertilised eggs during segmentation in weak solutions of various poisons and narcotics, he was able to induce the defect. The result only followed if the time of treatment included quite early stages of development, well before the onset of chemo-differentiation. The natural supposition would be that there was a region predetermined to give rise to the structures at the extreme front end of the head, and that this region was especially sensitive, so as to be completely put out of action by narcotic drugs. But this would conflict with all the facts previously discovered as to the lack of predetermination in the egg and segmentation stages.

Before we go on to discuss the possible solution, it will be better to look into the differentiation of one or two other organs which supply us with important clues.

The fore-limbs of newts and salamanders arise as buds immediately behind the head region. Various experiments show that the potency of forming limbs is confined to a definite area of the flank. It is most intense near the centre (as a matter of fact, as one would expect on the gradient

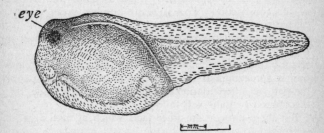

FIG. 17.—Cyclopic frog tadpole, produced by treatment of the early gastrula with lithium chloride. There is only a single median eye, which is beneath the surface and is here seen through the body wall.   (*From Child, after Bellamy.*)

theory, somewhat anterior and a little dorsal to the centre) and diminishes from this spot outwards, until, beyond a certain limit, it ceases altogether. The same is true for the differentiation of the eye-lens in the toad *Bombinator*. In this animal, a normal lens arises from the epidermis only if the optic cup comes into contact with it, and at the place of contact. Grafting experiments show that neither is the potency of forming lens confined to just that one spot of epidermis with which the optic cup will come in contact, nor is it spread throughout the whole epidermis of the body. On the contrary, it is localised within a small area of epidermis on the side of the head, and is most intense in the centre, which is situated opposite the outgrowing eye-rudiment. When epidermis from the trunk is placed over the eye-region, no lens is formed; when a piece of head-skin is reversed so that a somewhat anterior region of epidermis is brought into contact with the eye, a lens is generated, but it is smaller than usual. The prettiest demonstration is provided by an experiment of the same sort, in which, however, care is taken to leave a small part of the eye-rudiment (primary optic vesicle) attached to the reversed bit of epidermis. When healing has taken place, we then have a small piece of optic cup in contact with the centre of the lens-forming area, a large piece in contact with part of its periphery. Lenses are accordingly formed in both situations; but the potency of lens-production being different in the different regions, an almost normal-sized lens is generated by the small fragment, whereas the large piece of optic cup can only elicit a much undersized organ.

I have used the word *potency* as a useful non-committal term; but it will have been obvious that the facts could best be explained on the assumption that some special chemical substance was produced within the area, and that its concentration diminished from the centre to the periphery. This, further, is just how we should expect that chemo-differentiation should operate—that conditions should be favourable for the production of one substance in one area, another in another, and that the concentration of the substance would decrease as one passes out in all directions from the central focus where conditions are most favourable to its production.

Next time any of my readers see a Gloucester Spot pig, let them observe that its spots appear to be formed in a similar way, by the spreading of pigment outwards from centres of pigment-production. The conditions for pigment-production seem to be more favourable in the skin than in the hairs, with the consequence that the spots consist of two concentric parts, an inner area in which both hair and skin are black, surrounded by a lighter ring in which dark skin shimmers through white hair.

This is not only the simplest hypothesis on which to account for the facts, it is up to the present the only one which will do so: and we will accordingly adopt it as a working theory.

On this basis, let us now try to see whether we can better picture to ourselves the processes occurring during the primary differentiation of the future nervous system and associated parts by the differentiator. The differentiator is a single agent, which we must provisionally suppose to act upon the neighbouring tissues by virtue of the stimulus due to its greater activity. Facts in support of this view are by no means lacking. Child found that anything which tended to raise the level of activity in the anterior cut surface of a piece of planarian increased the frequency of head-production from this surface, and *vice versâ*. Lund was able to reverse the normal polarity, as regards head-formation, of a piece of stem of the polyp Obelia by electrical stimulation. Child caused a piece of stem of another hydroid (Corymorpha) to de-differentiate and lose its inherent polarity by means of treatment with weak alcohol (see Fig. 15); when replaced in sea-water, it regenerated a polyp; but instead of the polyp being at the end of the piece which was near the original polyp end, as it would have if it had been allowed to regenerate without de-differentiation, it arose from the top—the region best supplied with oxygen since it lay farthest from the bottom of the vessel. In the amphibian egg, it appears that the stimulus of the sperm's entry sucks away pigment and water from the opposite side, and that this is the normal cause of an increased activity which in its turn determines the position of the future differentiator.

The differentiator's effect thus must remain the same throughout primary differentiation, or at most there can only be quantitative differences in the effects it exerts upon different parts, due either to change of its activity with time, or to diminution of its effect through distance.

The substratum upon which it acts, however, although its future fate is in a sense quite undetermined, does possess some organisation—in the shape of its gradient. And it is perfectly reasonable to suppose that the differentiator calls out different effects in different regions of the substrate because the differences in activity which characterise these various regions provide different conditions on which it may work. In that case a grafted piece taken from elsewhere before gastrulation and put into the path of the differentiator would have to take on its right relations with the rest of the gradient—a supposition easy to make if the piece is small and therefore exposed to large remodelling influences, and one which we have seen tallies with the facts.

In any case, that the gradient must have an effect in determining the course of differentiation is shown by still another experiment of Spemann's, that of cutting embryos in half in a median plane after gastrulation had started, but before differentiation had been determined. When this was done, in each half the whole of the cut surfaces came in contact so that the top of the animal hemisphere was touching the opposite part of the gastrula, namely, the bottom of the vegetative hemisphere. Imagine an indiarubber ball bisected, and the cut edges sticking together, as indeed they sometimes actually do, and you have the picture. A slight rounding off of the two sharp projections at either end occurs, but otherwise the germ keeps its abnormal relation of parts. This being so, it remains to ask how the differentiator will act. If it acts merely by ordinary diffusion, the medullary plate should be straight. But if the gradient between the lip of the blastopore and animal pole has anything to say to the result, then, as this is now bent sharply round, the medullary plate and nerve-tube should also be bent. This is what actually happens, the medullary plate occupying almost exactly the part of the embryo which it would have done in normal circumstances, only deviating very slightly away from the cut edge.

We are thus justified in concluding that, in primary differentiation, the differentiator acts upon an already graded series of materials. However, it is also pretty clear that it is the relation of the different parts of this gradient to each other which also has a say in the result. Presumably the different substances produced in the first stage of chemo-differentiation grade into each other, and the limits of the future organs are determined by their threshold concentrations.

Let us now return to the cyclopia experiments. Child has shown for a large assortment of very various animals at very various stages of development, that the anterior end is especially susceptible to toxic agents, especially to narcotics and to specific inhibitors of oxidation. What Stockard presumably did, therefore, was to interfere with the anterior end of the axial gradient in his fish eggs, leaving the rest of it scarcely affected, owing to its much greater resistance. It should be said that when the dose of narcotic was increased beyond that needed to give cyclopia, the whole development became abnormal. This, we may

conclude, was due to the fact that the threshold of suscepti-
bility for the rest of the gradient was now exceeded.

After a ' cyclopia dose ' the highest point of the gradient
of activity would now lie in a region a little *behind* the animal
pole, the animal pole region itself having had its activity
depressed below this. The conditions necessary for realising
anterior structures would then not exist, so that, although
the structures are not pre-localised in any sharp way in the
cleavage stages, yet the effect resembles that which would
be caused by cutting out a wedge of tissue after differentiation
has started.

To sum up, we may say that the only essential differentiations present in the fertilised egg until after the stage
of gastrulation has begun, are the localisation of the future
differentiator region, and the existence of the main or
apico-basal gradient. Furthermore, that detailed chemical
differentiation does not begin till after gastrulation—a
point in interesting accordance with the fact long known
from hybridisation experiments—that the embryos resulting
from many crosses develop quite happily up to gastrulation,
but then show difficulties and derangements and often die:
presumably the chemical multifariousness of the hundreds
of genes has been wholly or nearly in abeyance during the
more physically-regulated segmentation, but now has to
emerge, and as a result the chemical incompatibility of the
maternal and paternal factors is revealed.

Once differentiation has been started, it proceeds automatically until the stage of function is reached. The limb-
bud develops into a limb when grafted on to other parts of
the organism, whether or not it has received its proper
or indeed any nerve-supply; and the hind-kidney of the chick
will develop a normal structure when its early rudiment is
cut out and grafted on to the embryonic membranes of another
egg.

Before concluding this section, one or two special points
should be mentioned. In the first place, the future differentiation of a particular region at a particular moment may be
of two kinds. It may be entirely independent of other organs,
in which case we speak of self-differentiation, or it may
depend upon some other organ, when it is called dependent
differentiation. In a sense, Spemann's work has shown us

that all differentiation is dependent—upon the differentiator; but we will, for our present purpose, leave this primary dependence out of account. Apart from this, self-differentiation is the most common, but dependent differentiation is of great interest, since it probably represents a primitive type of hormone action—although, since at this early stage of development there exists no blood-stream, the action can only take place between organs in contact or at least close proximity. The most clear-cut example of such dependence is found in the cornea, the transparent layer over the surface of the eye. This region only acquires its transparency and other special characteristics through contact with the main eye-rudiment. If part of the eye, through some abnormality of development, remains too deep below the surface, the cornea is only produced over the rest of the eye.

Many parts of the skeleton appear to be dependent in a simple mechanical way upon the development of other organs. The cartilaginous capsule of the ear, for instance, fits itself to the primary ear-vesicle, however that may be placed; and the extirpation of the eye-rudiment at an early stage causes the orbit region of the skull to lag behind in growth.

But the most curious case of dependent differentiation concerns the lens. Spemann showed for one species of frog (*Rana fusca*) that the lens would not develop unless the optic cup came into actual contact with the epidermis. The result was not unnaturally accepted as of general validity for the vertebrates. But data gradually accumulated which made this untenable; and, to cut a long story short, it was eventually found that all gradations were to be found from a condition of complete self-differentiation for the lens to one of completely dependent differentiation. What is more, the capacity for self-differentiation goes hand in hand with a greater localisation of lens-forming potencies, the completely independent lenses only being able to arise from a minute area, while those which are completely dependent can arise even from epidermis of the trunk, if this is grafted over optic cup, or if optic cup is grafted beneath it. We have already seen that in the toad *Bombinator* an intermediate condition obtains—there is some tendency to self-differentiation, which, however, in the absence of an optic cup, never

H

gives a full-sized lens. But the lens is not proportional to the size of the optic cup fragment in contact with it, as is the case with complete dependence; and lens-potency, in the stage of open medullary folds, is confined within a smallish area of the head. Both extremes of method are found within the single genus *Rana*, *Rana esculenta* having a self-differentiating lens !

This is a curious and, one is at first sight tempted to say, a discouraging state of affairs. But, although there is this great apparent diversity of method, it is probable or at least possible that it depends upon a quite small primary alteration. It is clear that the differentiation of lateral organs like the lens (which, too, never develop until some time after the primary organs—neural tube, notochord, and muscle-segments), although it may appear independent, is really in some way dependent upon this primary formation of structure. Presumably the system of gradients, which continues to exist, although possibly modified in detail, again interacts with the differentiating stimulus spreading sideways and downwards from the dorsal mid-line. If, in the case of the lens, this effect is exerted very early, then we have apparent self-differentiation; but if it is delayed, the region through which the differentiation-producing influence must spread is already transformed into the optic vesicle. If these considerations are correct, then the difference between the two types of lens-formation is only a matter of time, of early or late differentiation. The one thing which we do learn as a new fact, and an important one, is that contact is necessary for the passage of the differentiating stimulus.

A very interesting case of dependent differentiation has recently been discovered by Drew. If the tissue of kidney-tubules is grown *in vitro* quite alone, it produces merely flat sheets of undifferentiated material. If, however, connective tissue be added, the tubule tissue will differentiate and actually produce tubules (Fig. 18b). Clearly the connective tissue must exert some needful chemical stimulus on the epithelium.

As regards later stages of embryonic differentiation, Harrison and his pupils have given us results comparable in their importance with those of Spemann and his school for the start of the process.

Here I have only space to mention two points of especial interest for general theory. The tadpole, like all aquatic vertebrates, is provided with a special set of sense-organs in the shape of the so-called lateral line. During development, this grows out from the head, and extends along the middle of the flank. In the course of his grafting experiments with frog embryos some time before hatching, Harrison

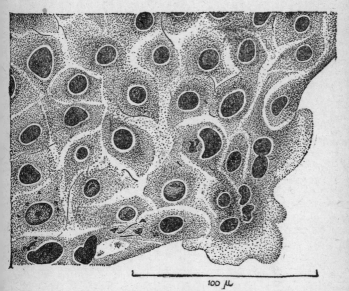

FIG. 18a.—Kidney-tubule tissue grown *in vitro* and de-differentiated. All the cells are alike and devoid of special structure.

(*Re-drawn, after Drew.*)

was able to secure union between portions of two different species, in one case even succeeding in raising to maturity a frog whose anterior end belonged to one species, its posterior end to another. When the anterior end belonged to a darker species, it was easy to see how the lateral line grew down from it along the flank of the hinder, lighter part, and pursued its course in the correct position (Fig. 16b).

Other experiments also showed that there is a certain optimum position on the side of the body for the growth

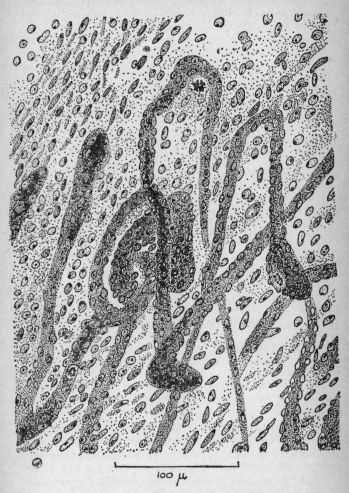

FIG. 18*b*.—Redifferentiation and formation of tubules by the same tissue on the introduction of connective tissue.

(*Re-drawn, after Drew.*)

of this organ, and the most natural supposition to make is that the dorso-ventral gradient has one level in which growth of lateral-line can best take place. This is especially clear when the front end of one embryo is grafted on to the middle of the back of another. The lateral line then bends round when it reaches the appropriate level (Fig. 19).

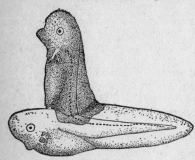

Fig. 19.—Anterior half of a *Rana sylvatica* tadpole grafted on to the back of an *R. palustris* tadpole. Note the lateral line.
(*Re-drawn, after Harrison.*)

That there is such a thing as a dorso-ventral gradient is further made extremely probable by Harrison's experiments on grafting limb-buds into various positions. His results may be very briefly summed up by saying that the limb-bud at the time of its first appearance already carries within itself a gradient from head to tail (presumably determined early by the powerful main gradient of the body), which in its turn determines absolutely the front and back sides of the future limb. When a limb-bud is taken and transplanted to the opposite side of the body, with its dorsal side still kept dorsal, it therefore follows that it will develop back to front, and point forwards instead of backwards.

But the differentiation in the direction from dorsal to ventral has not yet been established, but only occurs later, during the growing out of the bud to form a limb. Thus, however a limb-bud is turned—through 90 degrees either way or through 180 degrees to complete inversion—it will always develop with its structurally dorsal border on the actual dorsal side.

More recent work makes it probable that if the future limb area is grafted early enough, even the head-to-tail gradient is not fully determined in it, but arises after grafting n reference to that of the surrounding tissues. Thus here again the course of differentiation is determined, under certain experimental conditions, by the time-sequence of two differentiating processes.

Finally, we come to the effect of function upon differentiation. Roux in the '80's pointed out that two main periods could be distinguished in the development of every organ and tissue—the prefunctional or embryonic, and the functional. The latter differs from the former not only in that the tissues are capable of their definitive function, but that this function is necessary sometimes even for their maintenance, always for their full degree of normal development. As a consequence of this, if function is interfered with or altered, abnormal development will be the result.

One of the simplest and yet most interesting cases of the result of function is seen in connective tissue—in which the presence of fibres gives tensile strength. Tendons and sinews are clearly a very specialised type of connective tissues, joining muscles with the bones on which they pull; in them, the fibres are numerous and strong, and all arranged not only parallel with each other, but in the direction of the greatest tension.

When it is remembered that each particular tendon is arranged so that it lies in the direction of maximum tension which its muscle can exert, we feel at first blush so overwhelmed with the appalling accuracy of adaptation, that we are almost tempted to fall back on the arguments of Paley and his school, and say that such purposeful and detailed adaptation of means to ends *must* imply an intelligent designer. Analysis and experiment, however, have very considerably simplified the problem. If a tendon of an animal, such as the achilles tendon, be cut, within a few months normal function and nearly normal structure is restored. Examination shows that into the space between the cut ends, filled at the start with clotted blood, debris, and phagocytes, there grow connective tissue cells from the fascia at the sides, and new tendon fibres from the cut ends. At first their arrangement is irregular; then a meshwork of doubly interlacing diagonal strands; finally a simple parallel bundle of fibres. This last stage is only attained when the new fibres have reached from one cut end to the other, so that continuous pull is possible.

If the nerve to the muscle be also cut, the muscle gradually degenerates. However, it meanwhile shrinks considerably, and this also exerts a pull on the *new* tissue. In this case, although a tendon-like structure running in the normal direction is produced, its thickness is much less.

If the muscle to which the tendon runs is also removed, the differentiation of new fibre-tissue is much delayed, the final course of the fibres is irregular, and the amount of new fibrous tissue is smaller, so that nothing which resembles a tendon is formed. But if at the same time one end of a silk thread is left in the space between the two cut ends of the tendon, so that its direction is transverse to the axis of the tendon, and, when it is healed in, constant gentle tension is exerted on its free end (by means of a simple mechanical device), then a band of parallel fibres is produced—but it runs at right angles to the normal direction—an artificial and non-adaptive tendon !

Again, Lange led a silk thread from a human muscle to a bone, and sewed it there; after a few weeks' function of the muscle, with consequent tension on the thread and the irregular connective tissue which had grown round it, this tissue gradually took on the structure and function of a sinew, and became sharply marked off from the surrounding connective tissue.

Of recent years, numerous observers have found that the loose type of connective tissue cells called *mesenchyme*, in tissue culture develop fibrils within themselves along any lines of tension; and the same appears true for some other kinds of cells.

It thus seems clear that the irregular cells of ordinary connective tissue become spindle-shaped and fibrillar in the direction of tension if tension is applied; and that this accounts for many of the results observed. Something else, however, must come into play to account for the reorganisation of one type of fibre-arrangement to another when the tensile forces alter. Here it is probable that Roux's trophic theory holds. Roux supposed that in the case of connective and supporting tissues in general, certain conditions of tension or pressure or both were most favourable for cell-growth and multiplication. If this were so, then by a process of natural selection (differing only from the process described by Darwin in taking place between tissues and cells within a single animal, instead of between whole organisms in the light of day) all fibres would be eliminated save those which grew so as to be oriented in these particular directions.

Let it, however, be remembered that whatever theory be adopted, the fact remains that the fibres *do* become arranged in the direction of the greatest tension, whether this tension be normal or experimentally produced, whether the result be useful or useless to the organism.

Thus tendons are composed of parallel fibres, run in the direction of greatest tension, and are of size proportional to the tension exerted upon them, *because* connective tissue is of such a nature that the tension exerted by contracting muscles will produce just exactly these changes in it. The one fact of response to tension accounts for all the thousand and one adaptations of all the particular tendons in different parts of the body.

We again think of old Mother Carey, sitting idle all day, but making things make themselves !

Very similar processes are at work in the later development of bone, save that here development is favoured by pressure as well as by tension. The complex systems of struts at the two ends of a long bone are beautifully adapted to the pressures and tensions to which they are exposed in life. And if a broken bone is set not quite straight, these struts will unbuild themselves, and then become rebuilt in the mechanically most advantageous way. No other workable explanation of this than Roux's trophic theory has ever been advanced. The same holds good if two bones which should be separate become ankylosed or fused to form a permanently ' stiff joint.' In the connecting mass of bone a special architecture is developed, which, as has been shown by the aid of mechanical models, corresponds with an extraordinary degree of exactness to the lines of pressure and tension.

Now this type of bone-scaffolding is not developed solely in response to function, but is up to a point self-differentiating. However, what is given by embryonic differentiation without function, is never adapted *in detail* to the future pulls and thrusts, but only the broad lines of an architecture are laid down, to be later improved in detail, and often to be modified in quite important ways.

For instance, the examination of the bones of human feet, which through one pathological reason or another have never been used, reveals the interesting fact that their architecture is far more simian than that of the normal foot. Embryonic differentiation thus in man produces a bone-structure in the foot which is still more or less adapted to an arboreal life: but all traces of this are normally removed by long years of walking. Here, then, the finer architecture of the human foot-bones is not given by hereditary self-differentiation, but this is over-ridden in each generation by functional changes due to changed instincts. Thus here an apparently Lamarckian result is shown not to be really Lamarckian at all.

But use and disuse have also an extraordinary effect upon the size and proportions of the bones. When a puppy has one of its fore-legs strapped up before it begins to walk, it gets about quite comfortably on three legs. But after some months the fourth, unused leg presents a very different appearance from the others. The bones have grown considerably in length, although not up to their full size: in breadth, however, the growth has been but slight. This is of great importance, since it is the cross-sectional area of a bone which must be proportional to its load: thus it is clear that the adaptive relation which we normally always find between the cross-section of limb-bones and the weight to be supported by them is not the result of a pre-established harmony, but of a direct functional effect, pressure stimulating the growth of bone in a plane at right angles to the direction of pressure.

Fuld, again, investigated a puppy which had been born without fore-legs. The beast learned to progress quite actively by hopping: but as a result of this unusual method of loco-motion, the proportions of the skeleton altered somewhat, and altered towards those found in hopping animals like the kangaroo !

The blood-vessels have long been known to respond to changes of pressure. When, for instance, an artery is blocked, the increased pressure in its collateral branches eventually brings about their enlargement to a size sufficient to supply the needs of the region. Thus here again the adaptation between supply and demand is determined directly and mechanically. One or two cases have even been recorded in which the dorsal aorta itself, the main conduit of the body, has been occluded, and yet the lower part of the body has received a normal supply of blood—through the enlargement of some normally insignificant vessel.

Not only the size and the course of the main blood-vessels, but also the details of their branching seem to be mainly determined by hydrodynamic causes, so that the structure of the blood-system is in large measure self-created, just as the structure and form of a river-bed is created by the river's own flow.

There remains of course to be considered the difficult problems of broad phylogenetic differences in the structural plan of the blood-system between different groups of animals. Whereas the aortic arches of lower forms are symmetrical, a complete arch is only retained on one side in mammals and in birds. But whereas that side is the left in mammals, in birds it is the right. Is it possible to account for such differences on hydrodynamic grounds? The answer is for the present doubtful. No one has as yet sufficiently analysed the mechanical conditions prevailing in the heart of reptiles and developing birds and mammals. It might be found that the prime cause was some slight change of structure in the heart itself, sending the blood to one side or to the other; if later developments in the heart accentuated this difference, the flow might be directed overwhelmingly to left or to right. On the other hand, the tissues of which the degenerating half-arch were composed might be genetically altered so as to be predetermined to disappearance at a certain stage in development, as are the right ovaries of birds or the gills and tail of tadpoles. This is from analogy perhaps the most probable—that the broad outlines of plan are predetermined irrevocably, but that function develops all the details.

I have kept till the close some of the most startling and fundamental facts of functional alteration—those concerned with the differentiation of muscles and of the nervous system.

In tissue culture it has been found that the cells from which smooth muscle will arise resemble connective tissue cells in that fibrils develop in the direction of any tension; these fibres are, however, contractile, and if tension arises in a sheet of such cells in a culture, it begins to contract rhythmically. This in itself will account for many facts in the arrangement of muscle-fibres. However, not only direction of fibrils and of cells, but cell-multiplication and extent of differentiation depend, in considerable part at least, upon tension.

Carey established this by an ingenious experiment on a dog. Into its bladder he fixed a metal cannula, whose end could be connected with a vessel of fluid. By making this connection each day for longer and longer periods, and by placing the vessel at a gradually increasing height, more fluid at greater pressure was introduced into the bladder. Now, underlying the voiding of the bladder is a reflex mechanism: when a certain degree of fluid pressure obtains within it, and a certain consequent tension is reached in the muscle-cells of its walls, these (unless inhibited by voluntary effort) contract and expel the fluid.

Normally, of course, fluid accumulates but slowly in the bladder, and so the pressure rises slowly to the critical point. Here, however, more and more demands were made upon the muscles, until in a few weeks the organ was called upon, and had gained the capacity, to pass out over ten litres in a few hours. To do this, however, the contractions had to become more and more rapid, until finally the bladder became converted, physiologically speaking, into a heart-like organ, contracting rhythmically more than once a second when fluid was passed in under this pressure. At its most efficient, it could pump two hundred times a minute !

When, after a couple of months, the dog was sacrificed, it was found not only that the muscular walls of the bladder had increased in thickness to five times the normal thickness, but that the histological character of the cells had changed, cross-striations arising in them, and their whole appearance becoming more like that of heart-muscle.

Here again both the degree of differentiation and the amount of cell-multiplication depend upon the strength of the stimulus; but the example is of particular interest, since through artificial treatment the bladder was converted into an organ of greater efficiency and higher histological grade than the normal.

Although the heart will begin to pulsate even when no circulation is established, yet there can be little doubt that a great deal at least of its structure depends upon the amount of work which it is called upon to perform. If a developing heart could be called upon to perform only the intermittent work demanded of a bladder, there is every reason to suppose that the thickness of its walls would be much smaller, and the degree of differentiation of its cells would remain more primitive.

Finally, we come to the nervous system. At its earliest appearance, this is composed, like all other embryonic tissues, of roughly polygonal or cubical cells, showing no trace of differentiation. The adult nervous system, on the other hand, comprises the most elaborate central exchange mechanism, consisting of the cell-bodies and their branching and interlacing dendrites, together with the transmitting ' wires ' of the nerve-fibres both without and within the brain and cord—outside as the nerves, inside as the white matter. Not only this, but the nerve-fibres must run just to the right organs, the connections from spinal cord to brain and *vice versâ* must begin and end just at the right places, or the system would be no system but chaos and confusion. Furthermore, those parts of the brain and cord which have especially heavy function are large, those with little function are small. A familiar example of the former is seen in the spinal cord of the frog, which presents marked enlargements opposite the limbs; while the latter may be illustrated by the relation between acuity of smell and size of olfactory lobe of the brain, most mammals having large olfactory lobes, while in ' visual ' animals like monkeys and men its relative size is much reduced.

How is this order and this adaptation brought out of the bare rudiment which is all that is given at the close of the first period of differentiation ?

Harrison, in a fundamental experiment from which sprang the whole sub-science of tissue-culture, showed that if neuroblasts (as the nerve-forming cells of the embryonic nerve-tube are styled) are grown isolated from the body in nutrient fluid, they will yet send out their characteristic main fibre or axon-process, and also their short branching connecting switches or dendrites at the opposite pole. In fact the morphology of their differentiation will go on as in the body. But, as he was quick to point out, this tells us nothing as to the way they find their appointed stations.

Of recent years, Kappers, the Dutch neurologist, basing his ideas on the varying relative positions of different nerve-cell groups in different animals, has enunciated a principle with the formidable name of 'neurobiotaxis.' What this implies may be briefly stated. It implies firstly that the direction of the primary outgrowths of axon and dendrites are determined by the electric currents—infinitesimal in amount but important in results—which are to be found within the organism. Kappers was concerned mainly with the currents produced within the nervous system itself. His two chief conclusions are that when a bundle of fibres is formed within the central nervous system, the current it carries causes any differentiating neuroblasts in the neighbourhood to grow in a particular orientation—at right angles to the bundle—with their axon away from, their dendrites towards it. In the second place, if nerve-cells are repeatedly stimulated from one direction, the dendrites on that side will shorten, so that the cell-bodies move towards the source of stimulus. By this means, functionally interrelated centres within the nervous system will tend to become topographically approximated.

The theory was but a few years old when it received independent confirmation from experiment. Ingvar, working in Harrison's laboratory, was able to supply what had been lacking in Harrison's own earlier experiments. He grew neuroblasts in tissue-culture, some in the ordinary way, others under the influence of a minute electric current. Whereas the cell-processes in the control cultures grew out at random, in the others they were all oriented with reference to the direction of the current, the axon growing down the fall of potential, the dendrites up it. While experiment was thus making it extremely probable that the theory had a real basis, Child's idea of azial gradients was extending and amplifying it. So far, the theory only accounted for arrangements within a nervous system which had already begun differentiation, and had begun it in a characteristic and orderly way. How account for this beginning? Child and his school had already shown the existence of an axial gradient, at once morphological, physiological, and electrical, along the axis of the developing vertebrate embryo. This, and the subsidiary gradients from back to belly and from centre to sides, would suffice to set the outgrowths of the first-differentiated neuroblasts in the brain and cord growing in particular directions.

Finally, we cannot pass over the important researches of Detwiler, also carried out in Harrison's laboratory, on young embryos of the salamander amblystoma by transplanting limbs and pieces of spinal cord.

Detwiler found that when limb-buds were transplanted backwards on the same side of the body for one, two, three or four body-segments (somites), that their development during the non-functional period was the same in all situations. But after this, the degree of establishment of function grows less and less with the distance which the limb has been transplanted from its original position. This in its turn depends on the degree to which nerves from the proper level of the spinal cord enter into its supply. There is an interesting tendency for the limb-nerves to grow back towards the displaced grafted limb, indicating that there must be some attraction, presumably of a chemical nature, between them and their proper end-organs. But this attraction cannot be very powerful, for if a limb is transplanted four segments back, it is never supplied by any of its proper nerves, but by nerves from a more posterior level of the cord.

These nerves grow into the broad limb-bud; this narrows as it elongates; and the nerves, which would have stayed separated if they had supplied the skin and trunk-muscles, become concentrated and produce a network or plexus similar to that seen running to a normal limb. The existence of a plexus presumably facilitates unitary nervous control of the various muscles of the limb: but we see that it is brought into existence as a mechanical by-product of the limb's growth.

The size of the cross-section of the spinal cord in the late normal larva is much greater in the fore-limb region than four segments back. It is therefore of great interest to see whether this is determined, in whole or in part, by the fact of a limb being in nervous connection with the cord.

Careful measurements were therefore made of different regions of the cord; and it was found that the result of 'loading' the cord with a grafted limb was merely to increase the sensory part of the cord—the size of the sensory roots and the number of cells (chiefly in the dorsal-root ganglia) connected with the sensory fibres running in from the limb. Here, again, function helps determine the size of the part by stimulating the multiplication of the cells concerned. The rest of the cord, however, and in particular the motor areas and motor roots, show no increase in size, showing that the number of muscle-fibres to be supplied does not stimulate the growth of the supplying cells. This fact, together with the absence of any function in such limbs, led Detwiler to suppose that the limb-function and possibly the degree of neuroblast-multiplication depended on the fact that, in the normal course of events, stimuli concerned in fore-limb movement run up to the brain after entering the cord and then pass down again in fibres which normally end by making connection with the neuroblasts at the normal limb-level. The stimuli passing to the end of these would thus normally cause the excess growth of the motor-cells of the cord at this level.

But this supposition could be tested by cutting out a piece of the embryonic cord at the future limb-level and grafting in its place a piece from four segments further back in another embryo, leaving the limb-bud in place. The expected result followed. The nerves grew out and made connection with the limb; the expected hypertrophy of the sensory areas took place; the stimuli from the limb were transmitted up to the brain and back again: but this time they could reach the motor areas supplying the limb. Consequently, although the cord came from a region which normally remains small, the growth of its neuroblasts was activated, and it assumed the normal proportions of the cord at the fore-limb level.

Thus it is the quantity of impulses which *enter* growing nerve-cells, not the quantity of those which leave them, which determine the degree of their multiplication: and if we could understand what neurobiotactic action was at work to push the motor fibres down from the brain just so far along the cord and no further, we should have the relative degree of development of the parts of the spinal cord all determined on extremely simple principles.

At the close of this necessarily compressed and imperfect sketch, I would like you to look back for a moment and consider some of the facts in their relation to general biology. Let us first of all take the conclusions reached in the section on functional differentiation. Although Roux forty years ago pointed out in the clearest way the effects of the ' struggle of the parts ' within the organism, and although example after example of alteration due to function has been investigated, often with results far exceeding expectation, yet much misapprehension on the subject exists. Morphologists are often unwilling to believe in such far-reaching plasticity of structure, their *terra firma* in the invading sea of physiology; geneticists often look only at the beginning and end of the chain which starts in genes and ends in adult characters; physiologists often think only of the *analysis* of function, not of its effects on growth and the production of form. And this field as a whole has accordingly never received the attention or the general survey which it deserves.

I think that we are justified in saying to-day that a very large proportion of what we may call the general adaptations of the body are due to the fact that during the period of development an equilibrium is attained between those organs which are functionally interrelated. I do not intend to protest too much. It is obvious that numerous special adaptations cannot come under this head. But the fact that at first sight seems most overwhelmingly difficult to explain as due to natural causes, the fact that all over the body, in a thousand and one organs and structures, little and big, there exists harmony and a mutual adaptation of the various component parts—in size, in direction, in position, in packing, in mechanical efficiency, in intensity of working—all these myriad details of adaptation do not each require separate consideration, each a separate genesis guided in every particular by the hand of natural selection, but they all follow *en bloc* from a quite few inherent properties of the various kinds of cells which build up the body. At one stroke a huge and useless deck-cargo is cut adrift, and the ship of biological theory can ride the storm of fact without too great difficulty.

We are also able to see how a great many facts which are pointed to by the adherents of Lamarckian doctrines as impossible of comprehension on Darwinian principles but as necessarily products of inherited functional adaptation, are to be in reality explained. They *are* products of functional adaptation—not, however, inherited adaptations due to ancestral function, but acquired afresh in each generation through the everyday function of the individual. I have no doubt that many morphological points which are regarded by systematists as good specific or generic characters will turn out on analysis to be due to different functional modifications of an essentially similar rudiment. Indeed we have already seen that something of the sort holds for the distinction between the bony architecture of the human and the simian foot. Baldwin and Lloyd Morgan have given prominence to a similar idea in their theory of ' organic selection.' In this they state that new developments in evolution often start as changes in behaviour and instinct. The changed instinct induces changed function in each generation: but if a mutation were to occur which modified the organism from its start in the same direction, this would be advantageous and would be fixed in the race by natural selection. However, they have not extended their view far enough back into ontogeny to cover more than a fraction of the facts. Perhaps the position may be best summed up in the words of a well-known German ' Entwicklungsmechaniker,' who concludes a discussion of the problem by saying that until many more positive facts are obtained as to the so-called inheritance of acquired characters, ' we must look for the creative effects of function upon animal form, not in the history of the race, but in that of the individual.'

This same satisfactory parsimony of causes is also seen to operate in another sphere—that in which the form-regulating properties of the ductless glands are concerned. It is clear to-day that many, probably most, of the ductless glands secrete the same chemical substances in all vertebrates. The thyroid of a lamprey or of an ox is equally effective in inducing the metamorphosis of a tadpole as is the thyroid of the tadpole itself. Adrenalin has the same chemical composition wherever it is produced—through the whole vertebrate series; the posterior lobe of the pituitary, whether in sheep, fowl or herring, secretes a substance which can be substituted for that produced by the same organ of the frog and yet will cause the same specific darkening of the frog's skin; it is highly probable that the islet tissue of the pancreas, through its secretion insulin, exerts the same effect in all animals in which it is found; and at least possible that the internal secretions of the reproductive organ, the anterior lobe of the pituitary, and the cortex of the adrenal are also chemically constant from lowest fish up to man.

The vertebrate *quâ* vertebrate thus possesses what we may by a permissible metaphor call a constant type of chemical skeleton, just as it possesses a constant type of actual skeleton. On this chemical framework variations can be executed, just as they are on that of cartilage or bone. The ground-plan of the real skeleton of the limbs, say, remains essentially the same whether the limbs are used for swimming, running or flying, or whether they degenerate. So that of the chemical skeleton remains essentially constant, whether the thyroid, for instance, degenerates as in Typhlomolge, whether it remains almost functionless as in the axolotl, whether it exerts an effect on metamorphosis as in tadpoles, or on the growth of hair and skeleton and brain as in mammals and especially in man.

In passing, it may be observed that the ' chemical skeleton ' of a group is not confined to its internal secretions. Every zoologist knows how the arthropoids are marked off by the possession of chitin, the higher vertebrates by bone, the crustacea by the presence of copper instead of iron in their blood, and so on and so forth: it is merely in its form-moulding effects that the portion constituted by the ductless glands seems to be pre-eminent.

Sir Arthur Keith has drawn far-reaching conclusions from these facts. His conclusions, if I may summarise them in a way which is not quite his own, is that since in many related organisms each form-moulding internal secretion seems to act on the same general parts in the same general way, it is natural to suppose that, *ceteris paribus*, an alteration in the quantitative balance of the various secretions will result in an alteration in the structure and proportions of the organism. He further points out that whenever we can trace the effect of a hypo- or hyper-functioning of one of these glands, we find that it affects, not a single character, nor yet an unconnected random complex of characters, but a complex of characters linked together by being all related to the performance of a single function.

The pre-pituitary is thus related especially to skeletal development, excess leading, in the skull-region for instance, particularly to overgrowth of the parts concerned with jaw-movement. The gonads are concerned with the accessory and secondary characters of the two sexes; the thyroid in amphibia with the very diverse organs which change at metamorphosis, and so on. Thus when there takes place in evolution a change involving the correlated alteration of numerous parts, and yet one inexplicable on the simple functional scheme outlined above, we can often be absolved from the necessity of searching for its origin in a number of separate chance variations (which would make the correlation between them extremely difficult to understand), but can look rather to a single alteration in one of the ductless glands—a simple alteration with multiple effects.

There can, I think, be little doubt that such changes, productive of such effects, can and do occur. Many of the differences in proportion between related animals of the same group are probably due to this type of evolutionary change. Further, many characters appear to be secondary by-products of such changes. The antlers of deer are not only absolutely but relatively larger in large than in small specimens of the same species, and in large species than in small species within the group. This apparently depends on two causes—first that antler-growth is due to the same causes which are involved in general size-increase—perhaps the pituitary—and secondly that, like most secondary sexual characters, the responsiveness of the antler tissue to this substance is greater than that of the rest of the tissues, so that their growth is disproportionate: the greater the animal's absolute size the greater their relative size.

Or again, whenever vertebrate animals have attained a great size, there appear to have been two tendencies—one towards extra bone-growth in general, rendered visible in the form of rough bony surfaces and exostoses, the other towards localised bone-growth on the head, leading to the production of horns. Nopsca has drawn attention to numerous facts of this kind among extinct reptiles. He draws a conclusion similar to Keith's—that the excess size depends upon the activity of some gland, probably the pituitary, and that this agency's stimulating effect upon bone-growth is reflected in this superfluous proliferation.

Paleontologists will remember that so great an authority as H. F. Osborn claims that in at least three separate branches of the fossil ungulates known as Titanotheres, horns have become independently developed in the same place when a certain stage of evolution (marked chiefly by the attainment of a certain size) has been reached. This he wishes to ascribe to an inherent, predetermined evolutionary tendency, a mysterious directive power for which he uses Eimer's term orthogenesis. However, granted a general initial similarity of organisation, the facts would be expected if horn-growth was an indirect effect of size-increase. Under the direction of the pituitary, the mysterious orthogenetic power would fall to the ground; and in its place we merely have a single type of growth-mechanism necessarily reacting to increased size in the same way in all lines. The resulting horns would now be expected: but this point of view will necessitate a thorough revision of the current conceptions concerning our ideas of homology, or the correspondence of organs in different animals.

But in spite of this measure of approval for Keith's view, I think that we must point out certain important limitations in it. In my phrasing of his conclusions I said that quantitative changes in the ductless glands would, *ceteris paribus*, produce the required effects. Perhaps some will remember Lord Brougham's famous remark on the use of that phrase. ' Ceteris paribus be damned ! ' he exclaimed. Now this, as it happens, is an extremely good comment upon our particular biological problem. The *cetera* by no means always remain *paria*. As it takes two to make a quarrel, so it takes two to produce this kind of evolutionary reaction—the internal secretion on the one hand, the responding tissues on the other. In the course of this essay we have seen several instances of how the response of corresponding tissues or organs to the same chemical stimulus may differ in closely-related animals.

The total insensitiveness of the gills and fin of Necturus to thyroid secretion; the different behaviour of the limbs and the tail in urodeles and anurans, those two structures in the first case being independent of the thyroid, in the second brought under its influence—such examples should be enough to convince us of the danger of considering only one of the two partners to the reaction. Even Keith in his own examples (although once the mechanism is established, the results he postulates will flow from it) only removes one step further back the explanation of its origin. How is it, for instance, that of all the bones or the regions of the body, all apparently built in the same way of the same substance, some should be far more sensitive than others to the pituitary secretion? Still more remarkable, how is it that the secretion of the reproductive organ should, on the face of the male human being, stimulate the growth of hair upon one special region and not elsewhere, or that the secretion of the ovaries should encourage the growth during adolescence of just the uterus and its ducts, although they consist of the same types of tissue—muscular, nervous, connective, vascular, and so forth—as many other organs which yet remain unaffected? It is true that in the latter case the growth is probably dependent upon the increase of one tissue only, possibly the muscular, the rest simply keeping pace through that automatic functional adaptation we have already discussed, just as in the production of giants by the over-action of the pituitary during adolescence, it is perhaps only the bones which are directly stimulated to grow in length, the muscles and other organs following in the wake of the skeletal changes: none the less it remains clear that a specificity of that one particular tissue must be postulated to bring about the observed result—a specificity (if my supposition is correct) of the smooth muscle of the uterine tract to ovarian secretion, all other smooth muscle in the body remaining unaffected. This specific difference in the behaviour of particular tissues and particular regions is admirably illustrated in the change of tadpole to frog. This specificity, it appears quite certain, must be due to an inherited difference in the particular tissue, which, at the close of embryonic differentiation, must have attained a state chemically different from other similar tissues of the body. If there can exist such marked difference in sensitivity of one and the same organ to one and the same secretion in animals of the same class, as is seen in the varying reactions of amphibian limbs and tail to thyroid, it is clear that Keith's principle needs considerable restriction, especially in the indiscriminate application of it to morphology and anthropology by writers without the learning and insight of its propounder.

It is possible that the different races of mankind differ in their quantitative endocrine make-up, and that this difference is in its turn responsible for many of the morphological differences between them. But it is inconceivable that all or even a majority of these differences can be thus accounted for. No doubt but that the adrenals often stand in some causal relationship with pigmentation; but it is impossible to ascribe the dark colour of tropical races, as has actually been attempted, to adrenal alterations, without supposing a concomitant alteration in the reaction of the skin; and the latter is quite possibly the only agency at work. Extreme examples are often the most convincing; and I would like to ask the adherents of what may be called the purely endocrine theory of race-differentiation how they can account for the steatopygy or over-development of the buttocks in Hottentot women without assuming a special and inherited sensitivity of this region of the body, in the shape of a selective tendency to the accumulation of fat? Such special changes in particular regions or tissues cannot be due to quantitative changes in hormones. We must appeal to genetics, and suppose that they are due to mutations whose primary effect is not on the endocrine system at all.

In this connection it is well to remind writers who derive their knowledge of biology almost exclusively from a study of man and mammals, with a few other vertebrates in descending scale, that in the great group of insects not only is there as yet no evidence for the existence of any growth-controlling internal secretions of the vertebrate type, but that in one regard they have been definitely shown to be without any such hormone. I refer, of course, to the sex-hormone. In insects, the reproductive organs stand in no causal connection with the growth of the secondary sex characters. The sex characters of each tissue are independently determined by the balance of chromosomal genes or factors which the nuclei of its cells contain; thus it is possible in the case of abnormal distribution of the sex-chromosomes during development to obtain some parts of the body with the male-determining, others with the female-determining complement of chromosomes, with the result that a sex-mosaic or gynandromorph is the result. We know further that, in every class of animals whose genetic behaviour has been investigated, changes in single genes may produce alterations confined almost or wholly to a single organ, as when various mutations in one factor in the sex-chromosome of Drosophila produce various changes in eye-colour leading from normal red to white, while another factor-change in another chromosome alters it to purple.

We have therefore to consider detailed changes in special tissues, changes in general fundamental processes (such as intensity of oxidation), and changes in amount of specific growth-controlling secretions—all naturally determined in the long run by changes in chromosomal factors, but all acting in a different way during development.

There remains to be considered another method of simplification. Professor D'Arcy Thompson has pointed out in his interesting book *Growth and Form* that many differences between related animals can be reduced very largely to differences of growth along the various axes of the body. The form of one species of fish may be merely that of another distorted in a very simple way (Fig. 20). The skulls of three related species, again, may be all built on a closely similar structural plan, but one will be elongated and narrow, the second broad and short, the third deep and short—each one pulled out along a different system of Cartesian co-ordinates. If we could imagine some mechanism for accentuating growth-rate in any one direction without corresponding increase in the others, we should again be supplied with an agreeable parsimony of cause accounting for a multiplicity of effect. Such an explanation might also be offered for many of the types of human build and physiology, and has actually received much support from the work of Stockard and especially of Davenport. I may be pardoned for what sounds like (but perhaps is really not) a frivolous illustration. It happened that shortly after reading Professor Thompson's book, I went round St. Giles

Fair at Oxford, and there in due course penetrated into one of those booths lined with distorting mirrors. To my considerable interest I found that the mirror which broadened without lengthening converted me into a passable caricature of Mr. Winston Churchill; while the next one, which elongated without broadening, presented me with a startling likeness to the earlier period of Lord Birkenhead. I was able to console myself for this resemblance to two statesmen with whose policies I almost invariably find myself in disagreement, by reflecting that the construction of my skull

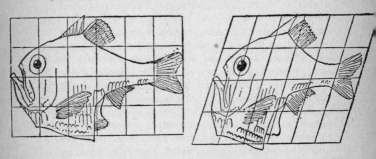

FIG. 20.—Outlines of two related species of fish (*Argyropeleaes olfersi* and *Sternoptyx diaphana*). The one can be derived from the other by a simple distortion; as shown in the two co-ordinate grids.　　　　　　　　　　　　　　(*After D'Arcy Thompson.*)

must be near the mean, from which their two extreme types were derived by extreme and doubtless exaggerated specialisation in one direction or the other.

It is in any event quite possible that alterations in the system of gradients which exist in the early embryo may account for alterations in the degree of growth in various planes, and zoologists would do well to turn their attention to what may well prove a fertile field for work.

Turning to a closely related problem, it is clear that the relative rates of growth of different organs, whatever the precise mechanism, are capable of being modified, and an inconsiderable quantitative modification in this respect may bring about far-reaching results. Of late years Goldschmidt especially has stressed this idea. To take a simple example, it is clear that the time of metamorphosis in tadpoles is determined by the relative growth-rates of thyroid gland and larval body-tissues. If the relative rate of thyroid growth is high, metamorphosis will take place in a few weeks, as in some American toads whose breeding-places are shallow pools liable to dry up before the summer is out: if low, then metamorphosis may be delayed for as long as two years, as with the great bull-frogs, which thus get launched on terrestrial life at a size putting them beyond competition with the young froglets of other species (Fig. 9).

The diminutive size of vestigial organs (such as the human tail) is usually not due to degenerative processes setting in during development, but simply to a relatively low growth-rate, which multiplies their bulk but a few times in comparison with the thousand- and ten-thousandfold growth of most tissues. Goldschmidt has pointed out an interesting corollary of this. The rate of growth is up to a point directly correlated with the degree of differentiation. Now in insects at least, as Goldschmidt himself has shown, periods of differing chemical activity may succeed each other during development. In moths, for example, the raw material of the different pigments of the wings are formed successively, *en masse*, and discharged *viâ* the blood to all parts of the body. They only become laid down as definitive pigment, however, in scales which are passing through a certain stage of differentiation; and as the scales in different regions of the wing develop at different rates and times, some take up into themselves one pigment, some another, and a pattern results which is determined by the different rates of development of different regions of the wing, and not by any localised differentiation of pigments themselves.

Now whenever one organ exerts a formative effect upon another, as with the optic cup and the lens, or the embryonic testes upon the original neutral or double-sexed system of sexual ducts, the stimulus to be effective must usually be exerted upon the dependent organ while it is in one particular phase of differentiation. Once it has got beyond this phase, it is no longer capable of response: and in a similar way the stimulating effect of the determining organ again is often confined to one stage in its existence. If the relative rate of development of the two organs were changed so that the proper phases no longer overlapped, the differentiation of the dependent organ would not take place at all.

That this kind of thing may actually happen is made probable by certain sexual abnormalities recently described by Crew in mammals, which receive a satisfactory explanation if we assume that the formation of testis secretion is delayed until the sensitive period for the differentiation of the internal sexual apparatus is partly or wholly past, so that some of their organs remain neutral instead of becoming masculine.

It will thus be seen that in all these ways the study of development gives us a new insight into the mode of evolutionary change.

Only by discovering the way in which the genes exert their effect during development can we fill the present large gap in our knowledge; and the study of development points out to us many of the ways in which we should expect them to act.

Finally, let us attempt to sum up in the briefest possible way something of what we have discovered about the development of a typical vertebrate. The first phase after fertilisation has a very simple function—to divide the material of the egg into cells of convenient size, and to establish a proper relation between nucleus and cytoplasm. Its course is determined chiefly by physical processes, and can be disarranged within wide limits without interfering with the normality of what comes after. It appears further that some part at least of gastrulation, together with the final differentiation of the three primary germ-layers from each other, also falls into this phase, which may thus best be defined as the phase of subdivision and rearrangement of material.

The next phase is that of primary or chemical differentiation. One particular portion of the embryo acts as an organiser or differentiator, and brings about irreversible chemical changes in embryonic tissues to which it is contiguous. The precise changes appear to be determined by two main causes—the degree of distance of the organiser on the one hand, and, on the other, the relative position of the tissue acted upon within a system of gradients pre-existing in the germ and derived from the unfertilised egg. The exact point of appearance of this organiser is to be sought in causes outside the original unfertilised egg, of which the point of sperm-entrance is normally the most important. It appears that slight initial differences in activity thus brought about by a stimulation external to the egg must multiply themselves during segmentation until the stimulated region has reached a high level of activity relative to the rest of the germ.

The result of primary differentiation is what we have spoken of as a chemical mosaic in which a series of separate parts lie side by side without any possibility of either humoral or nervous correlation between distant regions; mechanical pressure, strictly local chemical action, and the system of gradients are the only co-ordinating mechanisms.

Once this chemo-differentiation has been initiated, however, the gradients have little to say to it, and it runs its course with a fine automaticity. But the gradients still continue to operate in the undifferentiated regions of the embryo, and later differentiations appear to start in the same way in relation to them, and, once started, to run again irreversibly to their close. Thus the gradient-effect and the irreversible chemo-differentiation overlap in time, and continue to do so until the close of the embryonic or non-functional period, which is reached with the attainment of proper histological differentiation by the tissues, so that the organism can then begin to work in its characteristic way.

From now on four new processes come into play—the trophic influences of nerves; the circulation of growth-modifying internal secretions; differential growth along different axes; and the adaptational effect of function. This period is therefore that of growth, and of functional and of correlative differentiation. For brevity's sake we speak of it simply as the period of functional differentiation, which is not unjust, since growth and correlation are only made possible by the coming into function of nerves and blood-vessels and feeding mechanisms. The attainment of function by the organism as a whole does not of course prevent particular organs from differentiating later, in which case they will naturally pass through their own non-functional phase; so that here too there is an overlap of phases.

Distilling our results over again, we may say that the most fundamental process in ontogeny is that of chemo-differentiation. It is by means of this that all the essential characters of the organism are laid down—during the early phase of chemo-differentiation, those typical of the group to which it belongs; later on, its more specific distinctions. What goes before is preparatory to this: what follows, although of the greatest importance, is a playing of variations upon a theme irrevocably given. The later stages of development are thus in essentials regulatory, modifying in various and on the whole quantitative ways the primary and qualitatively-differentiated basis.

It is perhaps worth while observing that this regulatory function of higher mechanisms is seen also in the domain of pure physiology. Nervous impulses do not cause the heart to beat, but modify the heart's autonomous and original rate of beating. The thyroid, although responsible for the precise level of basal metabolism found in a human being, is only augmenting the rate of processes which occur, but more slowly, without it: and so forth.

The functional phase makes a finished organism out of a roughly blocked-out machine. It ensures most of the smooth running and final co-adaptation of parts. But the essential and distinctive criteria of the type, the species, and the individual are given as the outcome of a series of chemical reactions which are in no way the outcome of organic function, but its prerequisite.

You will perhaps have thought that I have strayed from my prescribed path, and that my frog has hopped too far from his own development. But it was part of my ambition to show the general application of some of the principles of development first unravelled in the amphibians, and to remind you that so common a spectacle as a tadpole's growth holds within itself secrets of greater moment than any sought after by the alchemist.

INDEX